TAKING THE STEP
SPIRITUAL PURIFICATION

You Can Change Your Life Today
The Secrets are Here!

TOSHU FUKAMI

Tachibana Shuppan

Published by Tachibana Publishing. Inc

No.6 Front Bldg.
3-42-19 Nishiogi-kita
Suginami-ku, Tokyo 167-0042, Japan
Tel. (03) 5310-2131
Fax. (03) 3397-9295

Printed in Japan

Translation, Book design and Layout
By MHR Planning
Cover Design by Shigeo Kawakami

CONTENTS

CHAPTER 1

Thoughts: What Are They, Really?

CHAPTER 2

How to Beat the Evil Spirits

CHAPTER 3

Spiritual Purification Can Change Your Luck in a Flash

CHAPTER 4

Secrets to Overcoming Karma and the Spiritual Purification of the Spirits of Aborted Babies

IF YOU WORSHIP THIS DIVINE
IMAGE,
YOU WILL BE ENDOWED WITH
SPIRITUAL POWER.

YAKUSHI NYORAI IMAGE

ILLUSTRATION BY
TOSHU FUKAMI

CHAPTER 1

Thoughts: What Are They, Really?

What Are Thoughts?

The world is said to be filled with spirits of all kinds. But ordinarily we cannot see these immaterial spirits as we can the bodies of other people, so it is impossible to confirm this assertion. That is why there are so many conflicting opinions in this regard. In this book I will try to explain in easy-to-understand fashion the principle of *jorei*, or the expulsion or exorcising of unwanted spirits – in other words spiritual purification. However, if you do not properly understand what these spirits are to begin with, then you will not be able to grasp correctly what *jorei* is all about and head off on a wrong tangent. So let us start by thinking about what these spirits we are talking about really are.

Spirits may be defined as spiritual entities that can exist either inside or outside the body. This definition may be a bit confusing, so let me put it a different way. Human beings are a combination of the flesh and the spirit. However, if you take the spirit out of the body, then even if that body still retained its life force it could not be properly regarded as a human being. It might be a "living creature" but it would lack any higher existence.

If that is so, then what really makes a human being a human being is the spirit.

What then is this essence that makes a human being a human being? It is the ability to conceptualize. As the French philosopher René Descartes succinctly put it in Latin, *Cogito, ergo sum* or "I think, therefore I am." And conceptualization boils down to thinking and judging. In other words, the capacity to formulate ideas or reflect....these are the ultimate proofs for laying claim to being human.

Be that as it may, thought processes as such are not limited to the human domain. Plants and animals have their own distinctive kinds of consciousness, their ways of thinking. Anyone who has ever owned a pet is well aware of this fact. But the human being was the first creature to achieve artistic, educational or religious sensibilities. And these emotions remain ours exclusively.

To put it in a nutshell, thought is the mother of culture.

Culture, this superior manifestation of thought, what more precisely should be called the godly in us, is the spiritual part of our being – in other words our soul. For that reason, a person who totally lacks the artistic, educational or religious dimension does not deserve to be called a human being; he is nothing more than a beast masquerading in the flesh of a man. And when such a man dies, he is destined for reincarnation as an animal. The reason is that he lacks the essential attributes of a man – "the lord of all creation." This is a point that Descartes did not explain. His error was that he did not realize that to truly understand human beings you cannot ignore the spiritual world and simply concentrate on the material.

If you understand this important point, then you will realize: The essence of humanity is to be found in its higher spirit, and the ultimate proof of the human is to be found in the ability to create cultural concepts. So to a certain degree "spirit" and "concept" are interchangeable terms. For example, a powerful spirit might be defined as a spirit that can express powerful thoughts. And the spirit of a man who thinks profound thoughts is profound in its own right.

Incidentally, if you look closely at the Chinese character read as "*nen*" in Japanese, which means "thought," "intention," "feeling" or "sensation," you will see that it consists of the character for "now" over the character for "heart" or "mind." Thus it basically means the state of the mind at a given moment. So the thought of the moment is true "*nen*."

As for the terms using the Chinese character for spirit, read as "*rei*" in Japanese, they are many and used to give a very precise definition to the various kinds of spirits. For example, there are *tatarirei* (vengeful ghosts), *jibakurei* (ghosts tied down to a certain geographical location by unresolved emotions), *ikiryo* (wraiths) and *yurei* (poltergeists in general). It all seems very complicated.

But if you think of these various phenomena as merely being manifestations of existing thoughts in the spiritual dimension, then this seemingly complicated classification becomes clear. Take the *tatarirei* for example. They are really nothing more than spirits possessed with the thought of exacting revenge.

It is frequently said that "ghosts remained trapped in this world." What that means is that feelings of resentment or vengeance remain behind when a person's spirit departs from this earth.

A person who departs for the Other Shore filled with regret will leave that regret behind as a legacy. If the place where the regret was left behind is a plot of land, then this spot acquires a karmic relation to the regret and is possessed by a ghost that haunts it. The spirit of the departed will find it chained down by its own resentment and regrets, unable to break away from this certain locale. And if the place in question is a house or other building, it becomes haunted by this spirit.

Furthermore, even when there are no special feelings of vengeance and resentment, if the soul of the deceased is not aware of his or her own demise, it may dazedly wander aimlessly throughout the spirit world, convinced it is still experiencing life. Such spirits are known as "wandering ghosts." These ghosts are doomed to wander so because they cannot or will not recognize what state they are truly in or the fact that when a human being dies he or she is as a matter of course supposed to move on to the spirit world. They express their rage and frustration by causing all kinds of harm to the living.

Then there are the departed who willingly cut all ties with this world and without hesitation move straight forward on the path into the spiritual world that was intended for them. That is the normal pattern and the one we are all destined to follow in the end.

When people die, they go to the spirit world. Those spirits who have recognized that they are supposed to start a brand new life as inhabitants of this spiritual world are normally referred to as *jobutsurei* or "spirits who have entered the blissful state." What this expression really means is that these souls have been cleansed and freed of all worldly thoughts and ideas and have attained Buddhahood.

Those souls who go beyond this stage and deepen their level of spiritual recognition, thoroughly cultivate a spirit of compassion and philosophic view of the phenomenal world, and achieve deep satori enlightenment of the mental faculties become what are known as bodhisattvas. These bodhisattvas have obtained the same level of enlightenment as the historical Buddha, Shakyamuni in his days as a seeker of the buddha way.

And those few bodhisattvas who come to possess the very highest form of enlightenment and can fully recognize their own spiritual imperturbability are fit to be called *Nyorai*. These *Nyorai*, or *tathagata*, are able to achieve a most perfect understanding of the true nature of all phenomena in the universe and because of their infinite compassion are compelled to assist all creatures in the material and spiritual worlds to attain salvation.

However, in order for spirits who have reached a very high state of development to be able to so help others, they must first transform the state that they recognize themselves to now be in, namely that of the bodhisattva, into an even higher state by becoming a *Nyorai*. It is only then that they can truly help others. And when a spirit manages to become a *Nyorai*, it also attains a state of divinity.

When I speak of godhood here I am referring to divinity as that term is used in Japan in reference to *kami*. The majesty of being of these spirits, who may even be living individuals, and their ability to exert their power outwardly makes them omnipotent and enhances their artistic nature. Such divine beings are beyond all the petty desires of human beings and have developed spiritual characteristics appropriate to their lofty supernatural position. In other words, they possess the love, wisdom and sense of the sublime appropriate to their position and can employ these gifts to affect things in our material world and accomplish what they will.

Some famous historical figures who can be listed in this category are the Zen monk Hakuin (1685-1768), the Chinese hermit and military strategist Chu-ke K'ung-ming (181-234), who is a hero in "Tale of the Three Kingdoms," and the famous upright official of the Heian Period, Sugawara Michizane (845-903), who became the patron deity of learning after his death.

The point to remember here is that spirits, both good and evil, are constantly intervening in human affairs in various ways. And we can basically categorize spirits as being "good" or "evil" depending on whether their intentions are for good or evil. Likewise, a spirit deserves to be ranked high or low depending on whether its intentions are culturally lofty or mundane. Furthermore, real deeds that truly affect the world come about when the desires are not just half-way, but are thoroughly heartfelt. Action can therefore be defined as expression of desires and thoughts harbored in the very bottom of the heart.

World Mate, an organization interested in spiritual matters of which I am the head, conducts regular seminars all over Japan. One theme we like to reiterate in these seminars is: "Changing your inner being is not the result of a slight adjustment in mental attitude or thinking. If your soul is truly transformed, your feelings, your way of talking and your patterns of behavior should change."

The term "soul" really encompasses all these things – our

speech, our feelings and our actual behavior. You might call these the upper, central and deep portions of the soul. And the deeper you go, the more closely intertwined you become with the spiritual and the divine.

All of this also bears on the theme of this book, namely spiritual purification of unwanted spirits. For example, if you want to exorcise an evil spirit, you must first replace the evil thoughts of that spirit so that it will be induced to enter into the life of the spiritual world thanks to a complete change in its manner of thinking and feeling. In other words, the process of changing the thinking of the spirit that has possessed a person, and emancipating that spirit, in itself represents the act of exorcising or driving out that evil spirit. So in a sense, what I am discussing here is closer to "redemption or emancipation of spirits" than "spiritual purification of spirits."

Self-control of Desires Is the Key to Spirituality

There are innumerable instances in which people suffer at the hands of spirits – in other words in which they are afflicted with a misfortune or disaster of some kind or another by an evil spirit.

"I suddenly felt unwell after paying a visit to the grave."

"Because some stranger seems to be standing by my pillow each night, I can't get a good night's sleep."

Sometimes such interventions from the beyond simply result in mild psychic damage to an individual. But at other times, without the least volition a person's hand suddenly will be torn from the steering wheel of a speeding car, resulting in his or her death. Or a person will spasmodically jump to his or her death from the top of a building.

And it is only later that it is discovered that many similar accidents had happened at that exact same point on the road or that particular building was infamous for its many suicides. Such kinds of incidents are by no means uncommon. And as I am sure my readers are aware, recently there has been a spate of aircraft accidents. Many people would no doubt attribute them to mere statistical probability. But things are not always that simple. Actually, it is more logical to conclude that spirits have been at work here as well.

When spirits do become so involved, certain conditions must be present. And if those conditions are not present, then no matter what spirit is involved, it is not going to be able to influence human affairs. What exactly are these conditions? Most importantly, spiritual or emotional vibrations have to be flowing between the spirits and human beings in question. In other words, they have to be on the same wavelength.

Say for instance you want to watch a certain TV program. To do so you have to tune in to the proper frequency for the channel that is broadcasting it at a scheduled time. You have to be on the right wavelength. The same thing holds true for "sympathetic" spiritual waves. Only if a person is tuned into the same wavelength will a spirit be clearly able to influence him or her.

Of course, the "frequency" of spiritual wavelengths cannot be measured in megacycles of electricity. Rather the degree to which a person is attracted to a certain way of thinking or feeling will determine whether he or she sympathizes with it, actively advocates it or carries on interaction with like-minded spirits. For example, if persons are thinking dark thoughts, they are likely to be dragged down by evil spirits into a world of darkness.

If, on the other hand, persons should be steadfast in cultivating strong sentiments of benevolence and eagerness to seek the truth, then they will get on the same wavelengths as the bodhisattva Buddhist saints or *Nyorai (tathagata)* buddhas. And they will be able to engage in fortuitous interaction with spirits.

What I am basically saying is that any human intercourse with spirits, be they good or evil, of high or low level, in other words whether or not a person is possessed by one of the spirits, is ultimately dependent on the thoughts and sentiments that individual people guard in their hearts.

One of the first patriarchs of the T'ien-t'ai sect in China, Tendai in Japanese, named Chih-i (538-97), preached the theory of "3,000 realms in one thought." By this he meant that any thought or desire formulated in this present world gallops around the "three-thousand-great-thousandfold world" and depending on its nature a person's soul can be brought into spiritual contact with heavens or hells. In other words, he taught that through this process a person can himself become either a bodhisattva or a chum of perverse demon spirits. That is to say, a single thought of this moment can be a spiritual watershed, deciding whether you will end up on the side of good or evil, heaven or hell.

Consequently, if you are determined not to have anything to do with evil spirits, the first thing you have to do is make sure that you are well aware of what thoughts you have. And if it seems like you are harboring some suspicious thoughts, then you need to take drastic action by deeply reflecting on the situation and doing what is necessary to quickly correct that situation.

Just be aware that devils have lurked in some corner of the heart of every person who has lived. That goes for saints and sages as well as the average person. In fact the only difference between the saint or sage and the common man is a difference in ability to prevent action on the part of these devils and to forestall them from taking advantage of the person. This ability is acquired through knowledge and spiritual training that allows the sage or saint to be constantly on his guard. These men are thus able to drive depraved or vicious thoughts from their minds, and thus interrupt all contact with the unwanted evil spirits.

However, the necessary self-restraint is really not all that difficult. No doubt many of my readers are thinking that if that were really so, no one would be suffering today. But the truth is that this necessary self-control begins with a single conscious wish that it be so. And the fact is that once such a conscious thought takes shape, it can quickly result in the desired self-control, and thereby make everything much better. The key is to do everything early enough. It is much like recognizing the need for early treatment of cancer.

We have any number of terms incorporating the word "control." Take for example health control, self-control or even control football. Keep these examples in mind when considering how to handle evil spirits. The important point is that the first step towards expulsion of their wicked influence from your being is the conscious determination to exercise wholehearted self-control over your thoughts and intentions.

Will-power to Control the Spirits

However, determination to exercise such absolute self-control is not so easy to come by as it may sound. If you see some delicious looking food, you naturally want to sample it. If you see a naked woman, lustful thoughts are naturally going to assault you. Just about anyone who sees some money dropped on the ground is going to bend down, pick it up and put it in his pocket without even thinking about it. The normal tendency of human beings is to have their thinking greatly swayed by their environment and the demands of their five senses. Consequently, if you want your thoughts to go in the right direction, the first thing you need to do is to be prepared to do your utmost to create a healthy environment around yourself that will lead your thoughts and desires in the right direction. You also need to make an effort to surround yourself with people and things that will foster good thoughts and desires and will direct your five senses towards the good. This effort is what actually creates the basis for the required determination to exert single-minded self-control.

Shakyamuni, the historical Buddha, was born in a time and at a place where any effort by the individual to change his environment on his own was extremely difficult. Perhaps the main reason that this was so was that the caste system as it existed in India in the 7th century B.C. was totally inimical to such a personal effort to change one's environment. Clearly it was impossible to establish the necessary foundation for change. What Shakyamuni did was leave his home – actually a palace since he was born a prince – to seek enlightenment. After he had done so he preached to his followers the "Eightfold Path" to be followed by all who similarly sought enlightenment.

This original Buddhist code of conduct – requiring right understanding, right thought, right speech, right action, right livelihood, right effort, right mindfulness and right meditation – was quite severe and was really formulated with ascetics in mind, those who sought through this severe discipline to achieve ultimate satori or enlightenment. Faithful following of these precepts by people living in our modern world, where we are subject to a daily deluge of information and stimulation of various sorts, is clearly impossible.

By far the most important thing for the average individual trying to live in accordance with the "Eightfold Path" today is to understand what human existence is all about, by perceiving correctly in adherence with the principle of *gujumetsudo*, or "Four Noble Truths," and thereafter engaging in right thinking. By doing so that person will be able to avoid evil intentions and pursue the path of correct intentions, always alert to the threat of evil thoughts. If he then continuously strives his hardest to attain Nirvana or supreme enlightenment, he will as a matter of course be exhibiting right diligence. Pursued to the extreme, such a course of living would cause a person to become a mountain ascetic who lives and dies amidst nature far away from other men or a religious zealot who cares not at all for the mundane affairs of normal society.

But what would happen if a lot of ordinary citizens really started acting in accordance with the preaching of the Buddha? The average businessman would no longer be able to work for his company and firms would go under right and left. The financial system would become chaotic as loans remained uncollected. As tax collectors would no longer feel free to hunt down tax evaders, the percentage of taxes actually collected would plummet and revenue for the national government would dry up to a trickle as a result. This would naturally lead to a national fiscal crisis. Furthermore, young people would undoubtedly begin to view society as totally corrupt and the world as filled with scoundrels. They would want no part of the hypocrisy and vileness of society and would do everything possible to avoid getting involved in the affairs of the world, preferring to stay in school just as long as possible.

Should everyone adopt the "Eightfold Path" as their spiritual guideline, no one would seek to make his mark on the world or to gain the respect of his fellows by accomplishing great things. Generally only the children of rich parents have good luck with finances with their wealth being just handed to them. Young people who note this fact would be likely to conclude with sorrow that in a world like ours it is impossible to follow the Eightfold Path and still be a success and have a major impact on society. Such a situation could wreak havoc in free market economies which are based on the pursuit of profit. Executives working for large trading companies and other elite organizations who saw no possibility to get ahead properly might seek alternative employment, such as running a coffee house, or work with local government (except of course for the tax office) that would not interfere with adherence to the Eightfold Path. I can assure you that I have already met many young people who have decided on a similar course of action because they want to seriously pursue the Eightfold Path with all of their souls. I know this to be true.

But for the most part, the Eightfold Path is inappropriate for contemporary Japanese young people. At least that is the conclusion I have come to. That is because they would lose the traditional spirit of *Yamato damashii* that provided the courage for men to take action, look beyond the smaller evil, train themselves to seek the greatest good, and when necessary oppose the prevailing trends in society. The traditionally known "Kannagara no Michi" or "The Way of the Gods" teaches that if people become slightly tainted by evil all they have to do to get rid of it is to go through a purification ritual. They should obtain the courage and fortitude required to work for greater good. Thus, I think you can see how the significance of the Eightfold Path has changed greatly over the years.

Japanese culture has existed for some 2,000 years. It developed in generally positive, healthy fashion during that period because it was primarily imbued with the spirit of Shinto, also known as "The Way of the Gods." That is why the teachings of Buddhism, especially those of the Mahayana school, as reflected in the Nichiren and Amidist sects, have found such fertile soil in this country. They continue to flourish today. That is also why Zen, with its emphasis on personal magnanimity, resourcefulness and versatility, has established such deep roots in Japanese culture.

Also, the reason that primitive Hinayana (also known as Theravada) Buddhism – the precepts that facilitated Shakyamuni's attainment of enlightenment – has not greatly influenced Japanese culture is that Shinto was already thriving in Japan before

Buddhism reached its shores. The Eightfold Path is the heart of Hinayana Buddhism. But if it had been adopted wholesale by the Japanese, it would have caused the Japanese soul and spirit to become cramped and distorted. That would be especially true for young people who did not intend to become Buddhist priests. If they took the precepts of Hinayana Buddhism to heart when they were young, they would have been of absolutely no use to actual society. They would have become incapable of confronting evil in the real world.

I myself like to promote the Confucian philosophy of "four avoidances." These encourage avoidance of improper seeing, hearing, speaking and doing. They are something like an abbreviated version of the Eightfold Path, but cannot be considered as sublime a code of conduct as the former. Talking is certainly far easier than doing. But if people become too strict in regard to these avoidances, then the common sense needed for a society to function properly will be greatly diminished and a negative preoccupation with "perfectionism" will result.

In my books I am attempting to explain things as correctly as possible. That is why I have advised a brighter, more positive, more constructive way of looking at things. This was summed up in my earlier advice that you should work to establish a wonderful environment around yourself, that you should seek out contact with people and things that will induce in you healthy intentions, and that you should strive to direct your five senses towards the virtuous. What this amounts to is a personal attitude that values brightness, positiveness and development.

Next, I would like you to know that the desired control of the mind I discussed earlier manifests itself in the ability to distinguish various kinds of thoughts and to determine whether these thoughts are likely to attract good or evil spirits. I will tell you below exactly how you can easily identify which category a given thought belongs in and develop the habit of constantly differentiating the ideas and intentions that float through your mind.

First of all, remember that a virtuous idea is bright, forward-looking, positive, conducive to development and harmonious. On the other hand, an evil thought is dark, reactionary, negative, critical and suspicious. If you reach the point where you are able to tell the difference and immediately reject the evil in favor of the good, you will have achieved perfect control over your thoughts and intentions.

But how exactly can a person reach that stage? In this book I will try to explain some specific methods for doing just that. For example, I will discuss how to separate your thoughts from yourself and the importance of academic study for developing an ability to form virtuous thoughts. I will also introduce the proper method for chanting sutras and other useful techniques.

Spirits are entities that cannot be seen with the human eye. It is therefore difficult to verify their existence. But through spiritual development and a change in your way of thinking, based on total control of the mind, you can become a person who controls the spirits rather than being controlled by them. The purpose of the rest of this chapter is to explain how you can attain this new level. More specifically, my goal is to encourage a process of self-renewal in as many individuals as possible, so that they will not be in a position where they need to undergo a spiritual purification, but instead will be able to expel evil from themselves on their own.

Guardian Spirits and Inferior Spirits

Many people never are even aware of the fact that human beings and spirits are intimately linked together. There are certain principles in operation that tie the worlds of the spirits and men together. That is true for instance in the case of the guardian spirits.

The job of these particular spirits is to protect the person they have been assigned to, be he a saint, noble-hearted man or true villain.

The basic job of the guardian spirits is to help bring happiness to human beings and to help them to live in accordance with Heaven's plan for each individual. They represent a form of help from the spirit world to keep men on the straight and narrow path. A person's guardian spirit also holds principal responsibility for encouraging his personal spiritual development in virtue, through the vehicle of education.

I would point out that a person does not necessarily have only one guardian spirit. In fact, the average person has between ten and fifteen of them. In extreme cases a person may have forty, fifty or even more guardian spirits hovering around him. Strictly speaking, these spirits are known as "supportive spirits" and groups of them are referred to as "supportive spirit bands."

The guardian spirits who are best equipped to provide the kind of personal spiritual assistance that a person requires at any given moment for the sake of his spiritual development act as leaders at that point in time. That is why a person's entourage of guardian spirits can change up to four or five times during his lifetime – typically in infancy, adolescence and when he is in the prime of life. Of course, some people retain the same guardian spirits for their entire lifetime.

The primary guardian spirit acts as kind of a middle man between the individual and the supportive spirit band and a representative of the latter. As such this spirit is very powerful. We human beings are protected twenty four hours a day every day by these bands of virtuous guardian spirits. And they are on their guard at all times.

Now, I realize some of my readers have doubts in their mind. They are probably offering objections like the following:

"If that is true, then why are there evil people in this world?"

"Why is there so much unhappiness?"

"If such wonderful guardian spirits were really around to help everyone, wouldn't everyone be perfectly happy?"

"I don't care about the rest of the world, but why is it that I have to be so profoundly unhappy?"

These doubts are perfectly justified and many others could be raised as well. Let me attempt to respond to them.

Do not be mistaken, we certainly are attended by guardian spirits. But at the same time there are evil spirits around us that are seeking to take possession of our souls. Because these evil spirits, who are suffering in hell, seek to drag human beings down to their own level, bad fortune and unhappiness result.

Actually, the fundamental cause of unhappiness is to be discovered in the karma of each individual and his or her family. These unfortunate legacies from the past are what determine our spiritual fortunes. The evil spirits are only an exterior manifestation of this legacy. It is best to think of the existence of these evil spirits as rooted in other forms of evil.

Also, although we speak of "evil spirits" as a general classification, there are really many kinds of evil spirits about. Just to name a few of the most important, we have spirits which are tied to a specific geographical location, such as a haunted house; wandering spirits; apparitions of living persons; spirits of ancestors who have been condemned to hell; vengeful ghosts and the spirits of aborted fetuses. All of these, and others, possess living people and cause ill fortune and disasters. Of course, we should also include the evil thought vibrations that individuals themselves give off as a form of evil spirit, since they also do great harm.

There are many kinds of unhappiness in this world, far too many to list. The most important are no doubt death, illness, poverty and family discord. The direct cause of nearly all of them is malicious mischief on the part of evil spirits.

In other words, human beings have attached to themselves good spirits – their guardian spirits – but if their spiritual strength is deflected or weakened sufficiently, then evil spirits can move in. The good and evil spirits are thus constantly jockeying for the upper hand and their relative influence is reflected in the "spiritual report card" of an individual as seen from the perspective of the spiritual world. Whichever has the predominant influence at any given time will determine whether a person is happy or unhappy.

Guardian Spirits: How They Help

I would like to explain in more detail how our guardian spirits help us.

These spirits stand by us 24 hours a day, 365 days out of the year. They protect us both directly and indirectly.

The first type of protection involves the guardian spirits keeping a steady watch on our affairs from afar. When they protect us directly, they do so by displaying spiritual power given them by the divine world.

Those of us with psychic powers can see how the latter kind of protection takes place. When a supportive spirit band groups together to directly protect their charge, they form one enormous being, much like a consolidated robot or the giant in the story "Aladdin and the Magic Lamp." A highly trained stage artist has the ability to project this same kind of expansion of being; that is because of the spiritual backing they have.

Incidentally, whether the guardian spirits offer direct or indirect support depends on the conditions of the individual involved. Generally, if the person is being subjected to evil thinking caused by an evil spirit that has taken possession of them, so that he is not being diligent, hard working, progressive and self-improving, then the guardian spirits will adopt an indirect approach. If on the other hand a person exhibits a dauntless spirit in standing up on his own against evil spirits that threaten to beat him and fully recognizes his difficulties and is willing to face them directly, then the guardian spirits will jump in and intervene directly to help him.

On the other hand, that is not to say that when a person displays faint-heartedness or cowardice that results in getting him in a tight spot, the guardian spirits will not move to help him directly.

Why should that be? Why do the guardian spirits act like this?

The job of the guardian spirits is to protect the person they have been assigned to help. And when we are talking about a person, we are really talking about his core spirit or soul. This is what the guardian spirits are really concerned about. Consequently, when for example a person's heart is temporarily given to evil, and he is acting totally recklessly, the guardian spirits tend to look upon this as a learning experience that is necessary for the maturation of the person's soul. In such cases, they are still more than willing to directly intervene to help out.

However, no matter how much an individual may suffer, if the spirits determine that their intervention would tend to make that person too dependent and that getting involved would be detrimental to the person's personal growth, then the guardian spirits will just fold their arms and continue to provide only indirect support.

In a sense, these guardian spirits are like a wise father who is trying to bring up his children properly. He tries to use cool intelligence and wisdom and farsightedness to make the right decisions.

The evil spirits act in a completely different manner. These spirits are totally unconcerned about the spiritual progress and maturation of the person's soul. Since a spirit does not possess a body, when it takes possession of a person, it seeks to manipulate his thoughts, speech, actions and feelings. These spirits are merely concerned with satisfying their own desires and forcing the person to do exactly as they want.

However, the instant a person exhibits willingness to abandon the negative thoughts placed in his mind by an evil spirit, his guardian spirits will rush in to protect him directly for the first time. Of course, the supportive spirit band then drives out the evil spirits.

People should remember when they are in a fix that actually everything is being determined by their manner of living and resoluteness at any given point in time. So they should not adopt the attitude of others and automatically put the blame on meddling spirits.

People who are especially spiritually sensitive should pay special attention to this point.

Change Yourself, Change Your Luck

Spirits affect the lives of human beings in many ways, most directly in their personality traits.

People have dark or bright personalities, are decadent or forward-looking. There is infinite variety in the human family. And spirits have a lot to do with the process through which a person's character is formed.

For example, there are those people who can only think of themselves no matter what circumstances they find themselves in. They are incapable of even contemplating the happiness of others. You might say that such egotistical people are completely under the sway of evil spirits. As a result, their own personality defects trap them and limit their opportunities. For example, they cannot achieve what they might have through healthy social intercourse with their fellow men.

Some people can only recognize the negative in whatever they see or hear, so they never develop dreams, hopes or anything else positive. These "dark" individuals almost inevitably come under the strong influence of evil spirits. Their very personalities and negative ways of thinking sow the seeds of their own unhappiness.

The situation with bright, constructive people who want to help the world and their fellow men is the direct opposite. They are strongly influenced by their guardian spirits. Their thinking is bright and filled with love and concern for others. They are destined to enjoy a happy existence.

Of course, we all know how complicated and inexplicable human existence can be, so such a simple division is not really possible. There are egotistic but cheerful individuals and decadent, gloomy people, who still care deeply about the world and other people. Reality is often rather complicated. But bear in mind that no matter how tangled and intricate a situation may be, behind the scenes invisible spirits are constantly exerting an influence on the situation and the personality of the person involved. In addition, a conceptual world to match these personality traits is also being constructed at the same time. The atmosphere and types of spiritual vibrations given off by that conceptual world in turn determines what kind of spirits will be attracted to the person.

The Japanese word for personality traits is *seikaku*. It is quite instructive to break down the two Chinese characters that make up this compound. The character for *sei* is made up of the "heart" or "soul" radical and the character that means to be born. So, in effect *sei* refers to the soul we have when we are born. The character read as *kaku* means "to end in." So *seikaku* more or less means "what the soul a person was born with has become."

In other words, a person's personality is determined by the changes that have occurred in his soul since he was born.

Furthermore, this personality is the fountainhead of the thoughts or concepts of a person that at normal times give off spiritual vibrations.

However, the environment is not the only thing that has an

effect on the development of the personality. Parental discipline and the person's own propensities, as well as the thoughts, emotions and memories that develop in response to a given environment also play a major role in shaping the personality.

Even while the person's soul is being indelibly shaped by his thoughts and actions, it is also being marked by the intentions and spiritual energy of ancestral spirits, local spirits, guardian spirits and many other kinds of spirits. So in that sense, a good social environment and good spiritual environment are both essential for the development of a healthy personality.

What recourse then does the person who has already developed bad personality traits have?

Because the personality that a person has now is the result of the changes that have occurred in his soul from the time of his birth, if that person commits himself to developing a better soul through good actions, then he will still be able to develop positive personality characteristics.

This process is referred to as *shugyo* or "spiritual training." In other words, the person seeks to correct evil patterns of action, so that he sets out on a new course of good actions. He starts with his personal commitment and change of heart. Thereafter, he recommits himself daily through his actions and by learning how to exercise control over all his thoughts. Consequently, his entire personality begins to undergo a metamorphosis and the positive spiritual influence of his guardian spirits causes much greater effects. The reason is that nothing pleases guardian spirits more than to see a person try to help himself.

By the way, the kind of person who is receiving strong back-up from his guardian spirits rarely bears any prejudices, is cheerful, happy and positive. The very goodness of his personality attracts more and more good spirits, which in turn brings him more and more happiness.

Conversely, people who are being strongly influenced by evil spirits tend to be set in their ways, are gloomy and negative. As a result, evil spirits flock to them and they find themselves rolling farther and farther down the slope of misfortune.

If you find yourself in this latter group, I advise you to earnestly reform your personality traits as soon as possible.

However, when I say that, some doubtful people are no doubt going to respond, "If it really is so easy to change personality characteristics, I would certainly like to give it a try. I've wanted to do just that more times than I can remember, but it has never worked out. I just feel so pitiful, unable to change a thing about myself."

In such a case, you probably have to wait for the right opportunity. Usually that opportunity is provided by a change in environment that forces a change of personality traits or a sense of responsibility that demands change. Spiritual purification – or release of evil spirits if you will – which is the subject of this book, can prove the catalyst that causes the needed change of personality and clouds a person's future. Spiritual purification can be a great opportunity that makes the change of personality much easier. It can also serve as a shortcut to general good fortune.

The first of my ten books to date, *Divine Powers*, deals in some depth with the spirit world and spiritual purification. But in this book I would like to go into even more detail and look at the same subjects from different perspectives.

Honesty Is Essential

What exactly are these evil spirits – these vicious beings which seek to disguise our personality, estrange us from our guardian spirits and deny us happiness?

They may be divided into the following general classifications:

1. Apparitions of living people.

2. Spirits of aborted or miscarried fetuses.

3. Vengeful spirits out to avenge themselves on the descendants of whomever did them wrong.

4. Ancestors who died in an accident or suffered an abnormal death.

5. Ancestral spirits seeking release from hell.

6. Wandering ghosts seeking release from sadness or suffering.

7. Spirits in hell seeking release from the suffering they experienced at the time of their death.

8. Ghosts of haunted houses who seek companions in death.

9. *Inari* shrine foxes bent on harsh revenge against human beings for real or imagined offenses.

10. Water spirits that have transformed themselves into water serpent dragons to avenge the destruction of wells or other actions affecting their habitat.

11. Tree spirits of trees older than 100 years that were recklessly felled.

12. Serpent dragon gods or *tengu* monsters seeking revenge against those who felled sacred trees, destroyed shrines or committed some other religious abomination.

13. Spirits of birds, insects or other animals seeking retaliation against those who have engaged in wanton slaughter of animal life

14. Disorderly spirits of various kinds that gather around psychics and religious groups.

What can a person do to escape the influence of these evil spirits? First of all, you must learn to believe that your good personality characteristics represent the real you and that the traits that are dragging you in a negative direction are false. You must come to believe that the latter are the work of inferior evil spirits out to get you and that they really have nothing to do with the real you.

By continuing to deny completely the dark, oppressive,

decadent, negative characteristics that have been hurting you, you will be opening the door for positive personality characteristics to enter in naturally and change your life. Your guardian gods and spirits, as well as your tutelary deities, will join in to help your soul truly desire to develop positive personality characteristics, making you forward-looking, progressive, bright, artistic, harmonious and forgiving towards others. These after all are the characteristics we were all intended to have to begin with. You should try to believe that these are the only kinds of personality traits that you really should have. Such a belief will transform itself into tremendous willpower, which in turn will help you to drive away the evil spirits. You will drive them off through self-reliance. In this way you can distance yourself from thoughts you want nothing to do with.

However, I must admit that it is not so easy to reject negative personality traits. In order to do so, you must ensure that one vital condition is achieved. That is the maintenance of enough willpower to continue regarding your belief in your positive personality traits. If you do not have this required resoluteness of spirit, it will be totally impossible to reject your negative personality characteristics or achieve anything else of real value.

On the other hand, if you can develop such an indomitable spirit, it will become possible to clear away the negative things in your personality.

Let us consider the question of spiritual purification from that perspective. Well, when through resoluteness of willpower you get rid of all those negative personality characteristics and replace them with positive ones, you are in effect exorcising all of the evil spirits inside of you.

How then can a person go about acquiring this necessary resolute willpower? First of all, you must sincerely believe that resoluteness of willpower is something that we all have inside us to begin with. Then you must start engaging in action based on strong faith. And bear in mind the importance of keeping in good physical health, since the strength of a person's faith is partly determined by the strength of his or her body, muscles and nerves.

However, in many cases people who rely only on physical strength and personal convictions find it difficult to recover their resolute willpower after they once encounter a serious setback in life and lose their sense of hope. In order to develop strong fortitude and willpower that will not wilt in a crisis, it is necessary to constantly acquire learning, training and correct strong faith. By cultivating these three conditions, you will be able to discover the other you that is hidden inside you – the better you.

And how do we acquire learning, training and strong faith? Through the process of education.

"You mustn't think like an evil person."

"You mustn't have a dark and gloomy soul."

"Always keep struggling, cheerfully seeking to progress, always maintain a positive attitude."

"Be kind to other people."

People who have received this kind of discipline and education from when they were little children rarely fall under the influence of evil spirits. And even when they do, they usually are able to expel those spirits on their own.

Individuals who are uprightly educated from when they are small and thus acquire bright, positive, progressive personality traits already are living the kind of life that does not invite interference from evil spirits. You might say that they are constantly achieving a kind of natural exorcism. For that reason without any special reformation or struggle, they will be able to attract virtuous spirits which will provide them further support. But those people who have not received such an adequate education are vulnerable. So what can they do? They must put out extra effort to overcome the difficulties they face and hang in there when the going is tough. By doing so, by succeeding through their own efforts, they will be in a better position to lead and educate others than are those who had their education simply given to them without question.

In most cases the prime determinant as to whether or not a child receives an adequate education in spiritual terms depends on the education given them by their parents. Whether or not a person has been educated in such a way as to develop bright, upright, progressive character traits is the most important factor in determining whether he will become happy as an adult. The inculcation of these values is the responsibility of the parents. But I should note that among them honesty or uprightness is especially important. Therefore, I would like to discuss this virtue in some detail.

An analysis of the Chinese characters in the compound *sunao*, the Japanese word for honesty, reveals something very interesting. We learn that the root meaning of the word is complete truthfulness vis-a-vis the Supreme Creator of the Universe. It also connotes truthfulness to one's own soul, the most important part of a human being. In other words, honesty to God and one's self. God more than anyone else is pleased at the sight of a truly honest man or woman. But an individual's own interior spirits also rejoice when he or she is completely truthful. These spirits or *mitama* are manifestations of the primary soul. And the truly honest man will express this trait to the outside world through his actions.

An obstinate individual may have part of his *mitama* captured by evil spirits, but if he is honest, his guardian gods and spirits as well as other virtuous gods and spirits will be in the immediate proximity and will make sure that any spiritual interference from the evil spirits will be kept to a minimum.

Here once again I would emphasize the importance of a correct education.

Karma and Rebirth

It is important to point out however that it is easy to misunderstand the concept of education. That is because most people equate education with formal higher learning, and automatically assume that someone without formal academic training of a certain level is to a certain extent uneducated. But when I refer to education, I do not mean it in the narrow sense of academic learning. Education for me is discipline, the forging of proper personality traits, the forming of a well-rounded human being.

This being so, you are certain to find individuals who will defend themselves as follows:

"Sure enough I'm a scoundrel and totally lack an education. But it's all my parents' fault that I have such a miserable existence."

Such an argument is totally wrong.

If a person was born into a certain family, there is always a good reason for that. You have to conclude that this type who blames and complains about his parents is incapable of reflection and being honest with himself.

Why should this be so? To put it succinctly, it is due to the karma of a past life that is affecting the individual. Personal karma results from our actions in our past lives and helps determine what family we will be born into. Of course, karma is not the only factor involved in our lives, but it has a great impact on whether we will be attracted to good or evil. However, whether that tendency is confirmed in action in the present life will depend on the individual's each and every action and how much he endeavors to progress and be diligent. In other words, through conscious striving a person can overcome the natural drift towards a bad life and through persistent efforts can eliminate the effects of bad karma.

For example, let us assume that a person in a past life

committed grave crimes against his parents and the karma from those deeds is latent in his *mitama*. In that case, his parents in this life might treat him cruelly. It is simply a case of retribution for his sins of the past life. The local tutelary deity is responsible for choosing into which family a baby will be born. The individual soul has absolutely no say in the matter. So even if while in the spirit world he protests, "I don't want to be born into that family," he will be forced to become a member of it anyhow.

On the other hand, when it comes to the spirit of a person who in his past life properly regulated himself, engaged in spiritual training and followed a moral and ethical course, to a certain degree he will be given a say in the matter.

A good example immediately comes to mind. A rather famous Japanese pianist began training with virtuoso teachers from when she was only three years old. Heaven no doubt knew prior to her birth that she would be a prodigy and could acquire such training in this family; so that was why it was chosen for her.

Now let us see how this principle might work in the matter of inter-company personnel transfers and assignments.

Normally, when a highly competent employee comes up for a transfer, he will be consulted as to where he wants to be sent. His superiors might say to him for instance, "You've done an outstanding job in New York these last few years, so why don't you accept this assignment to Australia so you can relax for a bit."

But if the employee in question has not performed up to snuff and is being demoted as a result, he will not be consulted at all but only ordered to go some place.

Likewise, the actions of a soul in a previous life determine its standing in the spirit world. All of the good and evil karma that soul has acquired over all its previous existences will be weighed and the final assessment will determine what kind of circumstances that soul will be born into in its next life.

Actually, before a soul is reborn into the world, memories of its previous existences are wiped out so that it cannot remember anything of what went before. That is because if such memories were retained, in many cases they would hinder spiritual progress in the present existence.

Effort Is the Key to Control

I think it is clear from my explanation in the previous section that the education that an individual receives is not entirely up to his parents. If a person finds himself in a situation where his parents do not offer him an adequate education, it is really completely his own fault. But that is not any reason for giving up. Acquiring an adequate education in the end is entirely up to the individual. If a person wants to acquire such an education, he can do it anywhere. That is because it is not the kind of education that is dependent on whether you go to an academic institution or not. No matter where you might be you can advance your spiritual education if you really make the effort. One thing is certain: whether your karma from past lives is light or heavy, whether your parents were good to you or not, it is the height of stupidity to stop trying and to merely cry about your lousy luck in life.

The trick is to accept the situation as soon as possible and to make a commitment to start learning as much as you can each and every day – to keep striving for intellectual and spiritual improvement. Strive to see yourself through the eyes of the universal order we are part of.

Do so and you will get rid of the various inferior spirits that constantly lurk around you. Then your guardian gods and spirits and other good gods and spirits will materialize before you and your soul will become fully motivated. I guarantee you all this and more.

I would note here that in ancient times conditions concerning information flow and education were far inferior to how they are today. Yet people in those times tried extremely hard when it came to education and spiritual training. A phrase favored by the Confucians that I quoted in my earlier book *Your Place in the Divine Order* sums up their attitude on this point.

Although consisting of only eight Chinese characters, this saying has a very deep meaning. To wit: if you want to bring peace and order to the world, you must first see that your country is governed properly. If you want to govern your country properly, you must first ensure that your own family is functioning properly. If you want to ensure that your own family is functioning properly, you must first regulate everything concerning yourself. That is the meaning of this famous phrase.

Even though people in those olden days did not realize how to deal properly with spirits and the spirit world, because of their great respect for learning, training and morality, they were able to avoid many of the calamities that evil spirits intended for them.

In other words, the accumulated hard effort that is based on physical stamina, willpower and the proper frame of mind can drastically cut down on unwanted interference from malicious ancestor spirits, spirits tied to a particular geographical location, wandering spirits and various other kinds of evil spirits.

Be aware, however, that spirits seeking revenge against a family are especially vicious so they usually must be formally exorcised. But in other cases, a person's self-effort is usually sufficient to do the trick.

Incidentally, do not try to substitute a direct approach to the spirit world for proper faith based on study and disciplined training. Do so and you will gradually become a mere pawn of the spirits. And a person trapped in such a situation is very badly off. No matter how much you exorcise him, that person's thinking will continue to be held captive to the beckoning of evil spirits. For example, with a grumbling, carping, jealous, egotistical person, even if you perform a spiritual purification and get rid of the evil spirits that are controlling him, his soul will still be tuned into negative spiritual vibrations, so a new evil spirit will just step in to fill the newly created vacuum.

Visit a grave and evil spirits lurking in the area can take possession of you. Talk to someone who is possessed by evil spirits and the malevolent intruders might turn their attention to you. This often happens with people who do not have the requisite thinking and faith, built firmly on study and training that is required to withstand their onslaught. In this connection, I often tell people that there are three things they absolutely must not do regarding the spirits if they want to stay out of trouble. Let me tell you what they are. "Never show fear. Never pay attention to what they do. Never sympathize with them." Most often when people get taken in by one of the nasty spirits it is because they did not pay sufficient attention to one of these three principles.

So always be aware of this point as you constantly struggle to acquire knowledge and discipline yourself through training, so as to acquire a strong sense of faith. This is the key to making our souls happy and developing a spiritual glow. By doing so, you will create a "self" that automatically keeps evil spirits at a proper distance and will acquire an impressive band of supportive guardian spirits to help you in your righteous struggle. This is the secret to victory.

Memorial Services for Ancestors

Next I would like to discuss the interconnection between spiritual purification and memorial services for certain ancestors. Many people are very diligent about conducting services for their deceased ancestors. In fact, I am often asked how exactly these services should be handled.

In such cases, I answer as follows:

"It is enough to hold memorial services during thirty years for only your father, your mother and your blood uncles on your father's side. And there is no need to do so on a daily basis. Do so only on the first, third, seventh, thirteenth, twenty-fifth and thirty-third anniversaries of their deaths – six times in all. And then of course honor them during the *Obon* festival of the dead each summer. That is sufficient for personal memorial services. Your ancestors should just be honored collectively during the *Ohigan* autumn equinox festival."

My listeners usually express astonishment that this is really enough. Let me assure you it is.

Just think about it logically. If you try to pray to your ancestors one by one, you may make it through three or four of them. But their total number is as vast as the stars in the universe. Go back ten generations and you will find thousands of them, go back twenty generations and there are hundreds of thousands, thirty generations and you are already in the millions. And many of them are sure to be languishing in hell.

If you start conducting memorial services for each and every one of these ancestors, what do you think is going to happen? Well, for one thing your entire life is going to be taken up with such memorial services.

But that is not the only problem. People who are so preoccupied with holding memorial services while alive, after their deaths go to the part of the spirit world where they continue doing the same thing endlessly. Alive or dead their only raison d'être becomes memorial services.

As I wrote in *Divine Powers*, for thirty years after their death human beings remain at the crossroads of Heaven, known as the *yukai* – a kind of limbo nether zone, suspended between the world of the living and the true spirit world. Here they undergo a process of purification to wipe away the defilement they brought with them from the material world before moving on into the real spirit world. After they complete their solitary journey to the spirit world, their souls are ranked according to their spiritual balance sheet and they are assigned to either the domain of heaven, the *chuyukai* (the intermediate spirit world) or the domain of hell. Wherever they are sent, they immediately begin spiritual training, which preoccupies them until their next rebirth.

For that reason, it makes sense to only offer memorial services for a person during the thirty years during which he or she is at the crossroads of heaven or in the *yukai*. This is the only period during which they will have any beneficial effect. So there is no need to chase after your ancestors after they have moved on to the true spirit world, still trying to offer them comforting memorial services.

The thing is that unless the person performing a memorial service has been endowed with special divine powers, the ceremony is not going to help to the slightest degree an ancestor who has been in hell for a long time. On top of that, if you unwittingly lift the lid off of hell, you are going to have a multitude of evil spirits come swarming out. And they could cause your family any number of problems, including neurosis, serious illness or a rare disease. In the worst instances, they might even cause the break-up of a family. You could even bring a curse down on your head from the gods for your unwanted meddling.

So instead of getting involved in such memorial services, it would be much more worthwhile to concentrate your efforts on constantly developing your own wholesome character traits and a forward-looking view of life. By doing so you will be able to join the higher ranking of your ancestral spirits. This is by far the preferable course of action. Improving your soul so that you can join this group of illustrious ancestral spirits is clearly more important than holding memorial services for the spirits of ancestors who have been sent to hell. It will also have a much more beneficial impact on your personal fortunes.

But if you neglect your own education, training and development of a strong faith in favor of holding many of these useless memorial services, you will find yourself meandering in an endless night with no way out.

I hate to be repetitive, but I must once again emphasize that if you become preoccupied with memorial services, spirits of all kinds that are interested in their own release from suffering will come swarming around you, creating spiritual impediments for you and seeking to gain possession of your soul. You will then find yourself in a real blind alley.

Ancestral spirits who have been condemned to hell are liable to think, "Oh, boy. This guy is really into performing memorial services. If I can take possession of him, then maybe I can save myself." And that is exactly what they will do – take possession of your soul.

The real meaning of life is not to be found in holding memorial services. It is to improve your primary soul, your ultimate self, in other words to make your *mitama* spirits more beautiful, and to strive for a better world.

Of course, offerings are necessary, but should never be made in excess. This is the conclusion I have drawn from careful examination of the ways of the spirit world.

Improving the Mitama

So the goal is to make your inner self better. People are not born in order to become physically strong or to be able to work and earn a living. Of course, these are important facets of life. But in the end our ultimate purpose on earth is to do things in their intended proportions and to concentrate on developing a better spiritual self.

But how exactly do you go about doing that?

I can think of two possible orientations that this quest might take. One is the yin passive approach, the other the yang or active. In esoteric Buddhism the yin is frequently referred to as "the womb world." The yang is called "the diamond world." The first is a world of faith, wisdom and inward-oriented growth. The latter is a world of virtue, benevolence and outward-oriented development.

From this schema we can identify four possible orientations for personal development: inner-oriented development designed to improve the person's spirituality; thorough investigation of all natural phenomena, the gods, ghosts, and all forms of reality in order to fathom the ultimate truth; performance of all kinds of good services for the sake of the greater society so as to perform meritorious deeds for the gods and humankind; and, to display compassion towards all sentient beings and strive for the salvation of humankind.

The first method stresses improvement in our faith, knowledge and behavior concerning the gods. It is inward-oriented, spiritual and focuses on improvement of the soul. Of course, it has two aspects: self-improvement and help in becoming a better person provided by the divine and spiritual worlds. The first is dependent on environmental influences, the latter on congenital factors. Ideally a good balance will be struck between the two, what is referred to as the *myotei* or cardinal principle.

The second approach, thorough investigation of the ultimate truth, relies on accumulation of true knowledge about the eternal, universal, ultimate truth through study. This study should include great familiarity with the formless law preached by the historical Buddha, Shakyamuni, the "Way" spoken of by Confucius and the Tao of non-action and conformance to nature honored by Lao-tzu and the other Taoist sages. The knowledge we are discussing here is not information that will bolster "actualized knowledge." Rather it is study of fields like the classics, spiritualism and the intricacies of the spirit and divine worlds that enlighten us about the laws and principles of Heaven and expand our "latent knowledge." The better we can understand the ultimate truth, the more we can improve our own souls.

The third approach stresses active contributions to society. To do so we must have an honest and virtuous heart and do our best to accomplish work that will be of practical value to society. If we do so, the gods will recognize our contributions and store "heavenly treasures" on our behalf. Just as a company recognizes employees who have made outstanding contributions by promotions to the managerial level, the spirit and divine worlds honor virtuous individuals who work hard on behalf of others and thereby improve their own souls by bestowing on them heavenly titles.

The fourth approach, working for the salvation of all sentient beings through the maximum expression of love and benevolence, creates virtue, happiness and prosperity for you. This virtue translates into spiritual light of various kinds in the spirit world. The degree of virtue shining in your soul is directly proportionate to this light. It is also the same as the level of spiritual light in the "light world" in which the soul dwells. In addition, the virtue a person has earned will ensure that he is healthy and materially provided for after he returns to the spirit world and when he is once again reborn. Of course, the person who adopts the third approach also shares these benefits.

All four of these approaches demand self-improvement for a person's soul. But if you consider them carefully, as I already pointed out, they divide neatly into two groups. The first two are rooted in active self-improvement, while the latter two achieve this indirectly through the expression of benevolence.

Categorizing these approaches in Buddhistic terms, I would say that the first two would be Hinayana elements and the latter two Mahayana elements. In terms of esoteric Buddhism, the first two are Womb World elements, while the latter two are Diamond World elements. To put it in even simpler terms, the first two emphasize inner training and the second two focus on aiding others.

But it should be borne in mind that both elements are needed. If you concentrate on the Hinayana side, then you will be wanting elements of the Mahayana approaches and vice-versa. Only when both are working properly in tandem can you realize the truth. The first values calmness and the individual constitution; the latter values action and usefulness to others. Together they form the all-encompassing truth of the Buddha.

In other words, if you decide to improve your self by seeking to understand the ultimate principles of the universe and the ultimate truth and therefore study various things about the gods and Buddhas, you will find yourself committed to following the path laid out by them and committed to making society better and your fellow human beings happy. These goals will become your very reasons for existence. And from this starting point of keen awareness, you will launch yourself into activity designed to save others and improve society.

In addition, once you have developed this feeling and started to perform actions in the real world, you will discover to your chagrin that you are totally incapable of teaching others anything. You will become painfully aware of your ignorance and other shortcomings. You will see that in terms of knowledge or financial resources you have no social power whatsoever and you are undeserving of the respect of other men. No matter what fine talk you may indulge in, you are really incapable of leading others.

When you have reached this impasse, you will realize that in order to earn the respect of your fellow men, you must acquire understanding and insights into the ultimate truth, so that you may know how to lead others to salvation. Otherwise you will have no conception of what happiness means to others or of where and how to make improvements in society. Without spiritual development, you will be incapable of perceiving these things properly. So you will realize with humility that the only thing for you to do is to improve your self. If you do not do so you will hardly be in the position where you can become a counselor to others and offer them help in their own quest for salvation. In this regard, I would point out that even those who decide to take the road of the bodhisattvas of Mahayana Buddhism must also become well-versed in the concepts of "truth" and "the law" as propounded in Hinayana Buddhism.

For that reason, people who say that only Hinayana contains the true meaning of Buddhism, or those who claim that only Mahayana is worthy of belief are equally in the wrong. I must stress again, the two basic elements represented by these two streams of Buddhism are complementary, like two faces of the same coin, like the principles of yin and yang. And once a person comes to understand the true "Way," he can see that they are really one and the same.

I should also note that as a person fully develops his soul through these different approaches, his guardian gods and spirits will be replaced by those of a higher spiritual level. And naturally this new supportive spiritual band will do all it can to help him.

When a person reaches this point, we can for the first time say that he is a human being worthy of admiration.

Perfect Knowledge

Well, we are now going to enter a slightly difficult part of our discussion – an explanation of the Confucian expression that means "perfect understanding." I have not been able to find anyone who can give an accurate explanation of what this expression means.

Even scholars are sharply divided on the question. However, the spirit world enlightened me on this very point and I would like to share with you the general contents of that explanation.

The expression in question is made up of four Chinese characters, read in Japanese as "*kakubutsu chichi*." *Kaku* means "something that has reached its end." In this case, it refers to the extinction of all material desires and human wishes. *Butsu* means things.

The first *chi* means to end and the second signifies "knowledge" – in the sense of inherent knowledge. The great Neo-Confucian scholar Wang Yang-ming referred to it as "intuition." This is the kind of boundless inherent knowledge inside our souls when we are born. The first *chi* here means to cause something to be fully utilized and therefore to reach its natural fulfillment.

For that reason, the expression *kakubutsu chichi* really means: to extinguish desires so as to draw out innate knowledge and put it to its fullest use.

The phrase "When the heart is threatened, faith subsides" taken from the Confucian classic *"The Doctrine of the Mean"* that I quoted in *Your Place in the Divine Order* captures this meaning very well, I think.

This expression was said to have been passed down from the ancient sage rulers of China, Yao and Shun, and to constitute their most important secret teaching. The heart spoken of here is of course the human heart that is subject to so many passions in this material world.

So you can see that the first half of the expression refers to all dangers or passions that might affect human feelings. It also refers to the fact that all human enterprises carried out on the basis of actualized or revealed knowledge are subject to failure and that more than anything else material passions can wreak havoc with a person's efforts to achieve spiritual improvement.

The second part of the expression warns that the "god nature" and "Buddha nature" that originally exist in all of us and our souls can fade day by day due to life's temptations, until they gradually flicker out and become of no more use.

People are made of flesh and blood. So naturally the human heart is strongly attracted to things in the material world. However, when this propensity is abused, self-destruction can be the unfortunate result. How then should we act? We must be careful to protect the faint flame of our inner soul, and develop staunch faith. Saicho, the Buddhist priest who established a famous temple complex on Mt. Hiei near Kyoto, in one of his books spelled out the mission of that religious center. He wrote: "Faith is a treasure. And men of faith who put that faith into action through preaching should more than any others be considered national treasures. The prime goal of Mt. Hiei is to cultivate such national treasures."

I think this passage provides clear evidence that imbedded in Saicho's enormous store of knowledge was the aforementioned phrase from *The Doctrine of the Mean*. He clearly recognized the danger warned of there and had assimilated the message thoroughly.

I hope that you can now see the significance of this famous Chinese saying and also understand how it further explicates the true meaning of the expression *kakubutsu chichi*.

Roughly, it might be summed up as follows: To the greatest degree possible the passions of the heart should be controlled and by relying on the faith inherent within your inner soul learn to be strong and resolute in the face of temptation as you remain active in the world.

If you look at things from this perspective, I think it should be clear that my earlier advocacy of learning and training was not made solely for the sake of inculcating in you knowledge and analytical skills.

Another explanation of this way of thinking from a slightly different viewpoint is to be found in *The Analects* in a passage attributed to Confucius. "In olden days scholars studied to improve themselves, scholars today study to impress others."

In other words, scholars of the past studied in order to improve themselves, while the contemporaries of Confucius were preoccupied with making others take notice of their knowledge and analytical skills. That is the true meaning of this passage. It is a cry of near despair on the part of the sage.

Study has nothing to do with other people, its sole justification is to help make you a better, more complete person. It should protect and nourish that vulnerable flame of innate faith deep inside you. This is the true meaning of real learning, the true meaning of training, and the basis of ultimate true faith.

When a person does achieve this true kind of knowledge, then his god nature, Buddha nature, *mitama* and primary soul will always shine and bad family karma will not have an opportunity to cause any trouble. Consequently, evil spirits or other unwanted guests will not be able to bewitch that person. If such a person consistently manifests godlike and Buddha-like qualities in his life, the gods and Buddhas, as well as good spirits will always be tuned into his wave length and indicate to him the proper way to proceed.

For example, even if this person was born into a family with extremely bad karma and family relationships, if that person strives as hard as he can, he is guaranteed at least a certain degree of happiness. In fact quite a few such people rebound from their unfortunate positions to become major successes in the world.

No Half-way Measures

Confucius refused to discuss spirits and divinities. Why was that so? During the period when Confucius was alive, there was a wealth of local religious traditions in China. Explanations about the spirit world were rife and mutually interacted amongst each other. But Confucius dared to argue that men should consider things through *"this world"* eyes. And he did everything he could to turn the attention of people away from the profoundly mysterious to the mundane.

This attitude on the part of Confucius has much to teach us. That especially holds true for individuals who are over-fascinated with the spirit world, as well as many religious leaders and psychics. It would do them a world of good to absorb a bit of Confucius' "here and now" spirit, and engage in true study and training to strengthen their faith.

If that proves impossible, I would say that it would probably be better for such people to forget all about the spirits. The fact is that a half-way, ill-conceived interest in the spirit world has landed many people in the hospital – often a mental institution. Such individuals spurned serious study and spiritual training. They refused to accept that a battle was going on between their passions and their innate faith. And in the end they lost their core selves and became easy victims for evil spirits. If a person really wants to deeply understand the spirits, then he should first adopt the Confucian principle of keeping the spirits and gods at a distance, until he is sure that he has developed to the point where he can immediately fall back on his inner self should trouble arise.

To return to our discussion of Confucius, another famous Chinese sage and near contemporary of Confucius was Lao-tzu, who thought that Confucius placed far too much emphasis on the material world. In fact he was sent down by the Creator of the Universe to restore some balance to the scene. In enigmatic fashion Lao-tzu described to the world how the boundless, eternal, profound universe and the spirit world looked and functioned. Scholars are still fiercely debating what Lao-tzu's teachings really mean, in fact there is great controversy over the question of whether Confucius or Lao-tzu was really born first.

But I know for a fact because of my spiritual powers that Confucius antedated Lao-tzu. Lao-tzu was born about forty years after Confucius died and himself passed away at the age of 85. As I mentioned earlier, I only know these facts because of my special spiritual powers that allow me to look into the past and they give me a bird's-eye view of things from the perspective of the spirit world.

Several ancient Chinese books, including the *Chuang-tzu* and the *Li-shih* mention a meeting between Lao-tzu and Confucius in which the former instructed the latter on the true meaning of the concept known as the *Tao*, which he contended represented the fundamental order of the universe. But actually it was another person altogether who met Confucius; the muddled story got passed on to later generations as fact. In fact this other fellow, whose name was Ting Hsien Feng, was the real founder of Confucianism and Confucius was merely his disciple and successor.

The fact that Confucius was really a disciple of Ting was first revealed through Chinese communication directly with the spirit world. To that account I would just add the following information of my own.

At one point in *The Analects* there is a passage that uses a two-character Chinese compound pronounced as *roho* in Japanese. If you consult many different commentaries on *The Analects* you will find many different interpretations as to what this word really means. The meaning is not at all clear. Although the passage really remains a mystery, I think you could interpret the sentence as if Confucius were saying he respects something as much as he does *roho*. That would probably mean that *roho* is the name of a great teacher that Confucius himself respected very much. That description would fit Ting to a tee.

Confucius was already 50 when he became intimately acquainted with the *I Ching*, or *Book of Changes* – a volume that has had an immense influence on the spiritual traditions of East Asia. Only after reading this profound work did Confucius gain real insight into the laws and principles that regulate all in Heaven and Earth. The Analects state that Confucius read his copy of the *I Ching* so often that three leather covers for the book were worn out in the process. And the person who introduced Confucius to the book was none other than Ting himself.

In a sense, the relationship between the two men was much like that of John the Apostle and Jesus Christ. Christians would no doubt take exception to my views, but I think if you objectively read *The Book of Revelations* you will have to conclude that in terms of the profundity of spiritual wisdom and spiritual insights, John deserves to be ranked far higher than Jesus. But when it came to the ability to create and universalize a religion and save others, Jesus was far superior. John can be compared with Ting and Jesus with Confucius. A similar relationship occurred in the world of the Noh theater between Kanami and Zeami. The forerunner and the follower. The Womb World and the Diamond World. Origin and definition at the yin pole and completion and expansion at the yang pole. Each half of these famous pairs played its own special role in bringing to remarkable fulfillment part of the Supreme Creator's plan for the *Tao* and the expression of compassionate love.

Incidentally, in Chinese history, the schema for explaining the role of the gods, how the Supreme Creator came to be viewed by the people and teachings concerning salvation can be roughly divided into two streams; call them the yin and the yang if you like. The former is represented by the teachings of Lao-tzu, Chuang-tzu and other Taoists, the latter by Confucius and the later Confucians. Even though in this case the yin and yang seem to stand in opposition to one another, in fact they are closely interlinked. And in Chinese history they blended and supported each other in the fields of culture and politics. Later Buddhism was also introduced from India and three cultural strands became intertwined. The product of this mixing was the incredibly sophisticated civilization of the T'ang, Sung and Ming periods. Over time these three cultural strands were also introduced into Japan, where they played an important role in the cultural maturation that occurred during the Heian, Kamakura and Muromachi periods. In fact, they became the most important sources of foreign cultural stimulation for Japan's own unique civilization.

Distinguishing Among the Spirits

Well, I have strayed considerably from the main point, but if you have totally grasped what I have written about so far, you should be more or less safe from evil spirits. But there is another method for avoiding defeat at the hands of evil spirits that you should be aware of. That is knowing the proper way to judge what kind of spirit you are dealing with.

This technique is known in Japanese as *saniwa* and with it you can tell whether you are dealing with good or bad spirits or gods. However, unless you are endowed with considerable psychic powers you will not be able to perform *saniwa* successfully.

That is why I constantly warn people that it is very dangerous to approach the spirit world in slapdash fashion out of mere curiosity. Here, for your reference, I am simply going to explain some of the fundamental points that are paid attention to when distinguishing superior spirits from their inferior counterparts. For a more in-depth explanation, see *Divine Powers* in which I explain *saniwa* using the six major types of divine occult powers. Here let us just concentrate on the superior and inferior spirits.

One of the distinguishing features of superior spirits is that they

very seldom interfere with human beings or affairs in th
world. They do not go around telling people what to d
where to go or when. Instead of bossing, they usually lay the
groundwork in secret so that people will end up doing what they
want them to do anyhow.

The reason is that these superior spirits have been entrusted with
the education of us human beings. And pampering a person or
diverting him from blind alleys in the end hampers a person's
efforts to gain experience and grow. Such coddling might even
prevent a person from accomplishing his mission in life. So the
duty of these superior spirits is to make sure that the people
entrusted to their care have the opportunity to gain learning,
training and desirable character traits, so that they will enjoy social
experience and accomplishments. They do this from behind the
scenes by leading their charges in directions that will instill in them
a high degree of discernment.

Consequently, when a person prays for something that will
jeopardize the maturation of his inner being, his *mitama*, the
superior spirits watching out for him will turn a deaf ear to his pleas
– no matter how persistent they might be. In such cases, they will
be totally unbending and not lift a finger to help.

On the other hand, if the request involves one of the four
approaches to spiritual growth we spoke about earlier, these spirits
will be more than willing to help. In fact, they might move
positively even before the person has prayed for assistance. And of
course if the person actually does pray for help, the superior spirits
will be ready to offer a higher level of protection immediately.

On top of that, these superior spirits possess a highly evolved
sense of prescience regarding learning, training and their
connection to higher dimensions, as well as spiritual enlightenment
and a high degree of wisdom.

How then do evil spirits and inferior spirits treat people? Well to put it bluntly, they do not give a damn about the spiritual growth of people. Since they are not made of flesh and blood themselves, and only act as parasites by inhabiting another's body, they are solely concerned with manipulating that body as they see fit.

What it boils down to is that these inferior spirits are studies in unbridled passions and egotism. Unlike the superior spirits, they do not have the capability to assimilate things of value. In other words, they lack the abilities to explain things or place things in their proper perspective that derive from learning. All they know is what is right in front of them and they live from moment to moment. Naturally, these inferior spirits do not have the sensitivity to appreciate cultural refinements or souls capable of understanding the subtle nuances of human feelings. To sum it up, you would do best to think of these inferior spirits as having characteristics like those of the worse examples of human beings.

These spirits regret the fact that they do not have a body of their own, so they want to take charge of a living person's body. Consequently, they are always on the alert, eager to discover a crack in some person's spiritual armor, so that they can go rushing in.

They are given to whispering lies to the person they want to take possession of, such as, "I am a reincarnation of Saint Nichiren" or "I am an avatar of the Lord Buddha." This way they hope to take total possession of the individual's heart, spirit and body.

Because of their simplistic nature, if you always remain on the alert such evil spirits and inferior spirits who claim to be religious devotees will never be able to take advantage of you. Ironically, people who have a strong interest in spirits, or psychics and religious persons who frequently deal with them often become the victims of evil spirits. I guess it is a case of the cowboy getting lassoed himself.

Because their interest is fixed on the spirit world, such people end up seeing visions, hearing voices, and so on. They become convinced that these are august manifestations of the gods and Buddhas giving them spiritual guidance.

"You must act this way."

"Go to this grave."

When evil spirits give such orders through the medium of dreams, they are able to manipulate people at will.

Don't be fooled by such pronouncements from the spirit world. True superior spirits or the gods never handle things in this manner. They respect the free will of the individual, so they seek to influence a person slowly over time, while gradually enlightening him, making him conscious of what his proper mission is and deepening his spiritual insight.

If we look at the process by which the historical Buddha Shakyamuni achieved enlightenment and consciousness of his mission to save the world, we can clearly see all this. There was no sudden divine intervention. Of course, there are cases in which the gods dramatically reveal to a person what the divine order is all about. For example, such divine revelation was made to the founders of several native Japanese religions.

However, if you carefully investigate such cases, you will see that these people had spent a long time consolidating their spiritual foundations through spiritual training before they were ready for such direct revelations from the divine world. Also, when the gods made such direct revelations they often did so in the guise of golden or blue dragon gods. These dragon gods acted as a kind of medium for the message from high-level, divine spirits. The intervention from above in these cases was real and of a high order to be sure, but it could not match the kind shown in the life of the Buddha. The gods proved themselves to these Japanese by curing illness in their families or allowing them to perform outside miracles and so on as signs and encouragement for the propagation of their message. So we can hardly call these interventions low-level.

Nevertheless, Shakyamuni was operating at a much higher level of truth. Through his ability to transcend this level of intervention from the spirit and divine worlds, he was able to spread his message concerning the eternal, universal true law. Therefore, you might say that the type of divine spirit that reveals itself out of the blue to a human being to inform him of her of a divine mission is lower ranking than the kind that gently leads the person along and spends time to gradually enlighten that individual, as in the case of Shakyamuni.

As I explain in my book *The Divine World*, during the two or three centuries up until World War II, Japan was in a "dragon god age." That meant that in this period of feudalism and imperialism, strength and power were the key elements in society. Reflecting this situation, the spiritualists and religiously enlightened people who became prominent during this period all evidenced some of these characteristics. However, unfortunately many of them were deluded to some extent by *tengu* demons or dragon gods. There were however, around 30 people during the Meiji Period, most notably Oishi Korimasumio and Deguchi Onisaburo, who managed to avoid such pitfalls and receive direct guidance from the divine and spirit worlds. They were therefore able to pursue their own correct path of spiritual development and become religious sages.

However, the ranks of such true sages shrank to only five in the Taisho Period and seven in the Showa Period. Perhaps I should not need to point out that nearly all the famous religious leaders in Japanese history who received enlightenment from above did so not in the form of a sudden experience, a direct intervention by a deity, but rather through a gradual growth process. That holds true for Prince Shotoku, Enno Ozune, Gyoki, Kukai, Saicho, Sugawara Michizane, Nichiren and Shinran.

Just like Shakyamuni, their enlightenment and the entrustment to them of a divine mission was a gradual process. That was also true for the holy individuals of the Meiji, Taisho and Showa periods whom I referred to above.

Again I have strayed far from our discussion of the superior and inferior spirits. So let us return to that subject. I would like to consider a specific example in some detail.

In olden times in a certain place there was a man of religion who declared, "I am the reincarnation of a saint." Investigation into his case shows that he had had one of the sudden direct revelations from a god we discussed earlier, and as a result had achieved a certain degree of enlightenment and had been endowed with some psychic powers. Apparently, at the start the Kannon Bodhisattva revealed herself to him and made divine pronouncements to him as well. Or so he thought.

Some of these revelations from above indicated to him his evil or mistaken deeds, and in response the man sought to lead a pure and blameless life. It is also said that he became able to see his past lives and developed extraordinary psychic powers.

Now when his followers witnessed this change, they said to themselves, "This fellow previously was just a completely ordinary guy. Now suddenly he has received spiritual enlightenment and is able to display supernatural powers. Why can't I do the same? If I could just become like him..."

All these people started thinking like that. And maybe as a direct result each year a few dozen people from this community started claiming that they too were spiritualists.

The truth is that the "Kannon" who had revealed herself to the man was in fact a manifestation of the Blue Dragon King.

In almost all cases, Kannon guides people in a careful manner, helping them from when they are mere children to survive the trials and tribulations of life. Thus through experience in their family and society, these individuals are able to cultivate a sincere religious

...of religious mission.

...iled, concrete orders and relentless efforts to have
, things just a certain way, such as we saw in the case of
the "spiritualists" mentioned above, are the hallmarks of deception
by dragon gods or *tengu*. They are by no means indications of
involvement by superior spirits.

You can tell that psychics or religious leaders are under the
sway of the dragon kings or *Inari* fox spirits first by the fact that
they are more concerned with not committing evil deeds than in
spreading good as far and wide as possible. In other words, they are
negative rather than positive. Call them spiritual negativists if you
like. In other words, they are obsessed with the need to make other
people perfect and absolutely pure. As a result they have no respect
for freedom, magnanimity, or the sense of play and enjoyment in
the human heart. They lack that breadth of vision and concern for
spiritual freedom so pronounced in Taoist thought and the way
followers of Zen look at things.

These kinds of people love to carp. This food is taboo. This
feeling or that attitude are evil. That religion is bogus. They thrive
on rules and criticism. And they will not forgive what is evil or
unrighteous in their eyes. They act just like people did back in the
"dragon god age" of feudalism and imperialism. The fellow who
claimed to be the reincarnation of a saint acted exactly in this
manner.

But the fact is that true superior spirits are not all that concerned
with rules about food. Consuming meat or vegetables: they are both
fine as long as the taste is good and the ingredients are utilized in
the best manner possible. They also do not like to vehemently
criticize various religions and they are not concerned with
regulating the feelings and attitudes of people. Their benevolent
hearts seek to smother evil, so as to make possible the reform of a
person. And they are willing to take the time to do all this properly.

The education of small children calls for a somewhat different approach, but in general the way to deal with a person who is prone to evil thoughts and attitudes is to simply wait until those thoughts and attitudes have gotten him into sufficient trouble to want to make him change his ways. Then you step in to help. It is wrong to badger him: saying this is right or wrong, or do this or do that.

Instead gentle urging for him to reform should be pursued over time, showing him what the people around him think about him. The superior spirits realize this. They let these influences take their effect, so that the person in question ends up saying to himself, "Looks like you're really in a fix and have everyone thoroughly scandalized. Well, it looks like all you can do is turn over a new leaf and make the decision to lead a totally different kind of life from now on. Well, let's just give it a try!"

If the person has a true change of heart and is willing to set out on a new course, these spirits will back him to the hilt, encouraging him on: "That's great. Just hang in there. If you make the necessary changes in yourself, then your whole life will turn around."

These superior spirits will in this manner in forward-looking, understated fashion, without alarm or dire warnings, welcome the change of heart and enlightenment of such an individual. They will also go out of their way to give advice that will reinforce this enlightenment. This is exactly what happened in the case of Shakyamuni or those true religious leaders I referred to earlier.

Saints working to further the spread of Buddhism often relied on precisely this approach. By this you can see that it is odd to say that the fellow I mentioned earlier was the reincarnation of a saint. Saints arrive on earth with a mission, path to follow and point of view. Sometimes they may even be in part an angel acting as the direct messenger of the Supreme Creator. For that reason, even though Shakyamuni and other spiritual leaders have in a sense, been sent down from Heaven, that does not mean that they are special reincarnations. In cases where a person was a saint in the preceding life, you can expect that he will accomplish even more in life this time around – carry his previous mission forward. But if you analyze the spiritual messages that the person declaring to be the reincarnation of a saint transmits and his own preachings, you will discover that they do not have the requisite refinement and holiness characteristic of the thinking of superior spirits.

If you look at the holy men who have left a significant mark on history, you can clearly see that they have not demanded that people conduct lives of righteous perfection. Rather they have been concerned with relieving the suffering and troubles so intimately intertwined in the skein of life and in bringing salvation to their fellow men. They have attempted to do so by gradually raising the level of spiritual awareness among others and with kindness instilling deeply within them the wisdom that will allow them to free their spirits.

I believe that great religious leaders like Jesus Christ, Shakyamuni or Kukai adopted methods and approaches appropriate for the times they lived in. I have in mind specifically the fellow who bombastically declared himself a "reincarnation of a saint" in language that was a far cry from what a superior spirit would have used. If he had only truly sought in broad-minded fashion to provide definitive, positive, harmonious spiritual guidance to his fellow human beings, and had learned from the examples of those who went before him he might have proved able to accomplish much over time, since he was at heart far from being a wicked person. After maybe three years, the benevolent Blue Dragon King would not have abandoned him and thereafter snake and fox spirits or bands of scoundrel spirits probably would not have caused him any great tragedy. It is a pity that he did not follow his finer instincts.

Do not get me wrong, what I am writing here is not intended to be a personal attack on this man. That is far from my purpose. But the fact is that even though he wanted to give his all for the sake of his fellow men, as well as the gods and Buddhas, because he lacked sufficient knowledge about how to conduct *saniwa* with superior and inferior spirits, and because over time he did not take the trouble to evaluate the true significance of his encounter with "the divine," nor increase his knowledge of the gods, Buddhas and divine and spirit worlds, he ended up by struggling on with what he considered his divine mission.

And for that reason, he lost his original correct path and was unable to nurture his positive character traits. On the other hand, he dragged others into illusionary spirit worlds and at the same time suffered a flood of regret and suffering.

The reason I know this to be true is that I have dealt with countless spirits on countless occasions. At times I was skillfully deceived, at times I was made an ass of by these spirits; then again on occasion I suffered such physical pain I thought I would die. I had to draw on all the hard-won experience I had accumulated since I was a child and all I had studied about my forerunners in this field to cope with these situations. So I can understand how much this person I am referring to must have suffered, and my heart is filled with sympathy for him. In my own case, if my teacher Aiko Uematsu had not taught me so thoroughly concerning the secrets of *saniwa*, I myself would no doubt have become a pawn of the evil and dangerous spirits whom I was thoroughly convinced at that time were totally good.

The Basics of Saniwa

It must be admitted that discerning what is the proper path to take and whether a spirit is good or evil is by no means a simple task for the average person to undertake. Let me offer another for your edification. A female psychic on one occasion was meditating somewhere and experienced a trance-like state. Prior to that she had been very fond of books and she continued to read voraciously after the experience.

On one occasion when she was thinking about a book she had once read and things related to the author, her hand started writing on its own without her willing it to do so. And when she would start praying, she would fall into a trance and spiritual messages would come popping into her head one after the next. They came from eminent past spiritual leaders from around the world, including Japan. She herself came to believe that she was the author of a famous book concerning spiritual training.

Such instances seem to have become frequent of late. I even get a lot of literature and tapes in the mail containing "messages from the otherworld." Some months two or three of them arrive. Of course I can tell that they are all maliciously intended without even opening the mail. On one occasion the package I opened seemed to have a rather warm and comforting spiritual feeling to it. Only then did I discover that there was a spirit of a golden-fleece, nine-tail white fox inside. These are the type of things sent from the occult world that can easily pass as authentic.

So here I would like to inform my spiritually sensitive readers about the correct method for *saniwa*, lest they be taken in by such trickery. The first thing you must know is that superior spirits have made a vow that they will never introduce themselves with their former personal name as a means of making people believe in them. This is an important secret to know. The reason for this is they are not interested in being known to living people or having them feel grateful. Their concern is to carry out the will of the Supreme Creator and to act as his intermediary to make that will known to others. These are the things that bring them real joy. Besides, making themselves known to people actually decreases their stock of divine and spiritual merit.

Consequently, if a living person greets them, they will decline any personal recognition by saying that they are merely acting on behalf of the Supreme Creator and that this is what provides them pleasure. They will also explain that acting in this manner causes the gods to shower on them love, happiness and merit. They might add, "If you want to offer greetings, do so to the Supreme Creator. Should I accept such a greeting personally, it would result in Heavenly punishment for me. It would amount to accepting honor that is due only to the gods. Worst of all, the formless merit and glory bestowed on me up till now would all evaporate. We, better than anyone, know the retinues of the celestial beings and angels."

That is basically how these illustrious spirits are going to reply to your greetings.

No one who has really explored the truth is going to borrow someone else's name when making a spiritual pronouncement or pretend that something he himself has studied is actually the word of the gods or a superior spirit. These are simply not authentic messages. And if the spirit whose name was used was indeed a superior spirit, he won't be happy.

Normally superior spirits only have one thing in mind: they want to serve the will of the Supreme Creator, while protecting living human beings who have a Heaven-sent mission, and providing them with guidance and instruction. When a spiritual message is given to an individual in order to speed his spiritual education, it is not put into words for the sake of the world, unless that person does so himself. The merit involved goes not to the spirit who is doing the protecting and leading, but to the person who is being spiritually nurtured. It will be that person's charisma which draws others to him and allows him to try to save them and improve the world. The superior spirits in the virtuous spirit world have made a vow to act in accordance with this system.

There has never been an age – no matter how strong interest in the spirit world might be – in which spiritual leaders have said the spirit of the Buddha said this, or Jesus said this, or my guardian spirit said this, and people have just accepted it and the political, economic, cultural and educational systems have been reformed as a result.

True the Angel Gabriel made revelations to Mohammed and he spread them to society. But when The Prophet first did so he was a complete failure and during the night he had to flee from Mecca for his life on the hegira. Thereafter he changed tactics and allied himself with the people, fighting his own battles, and thus he was eventually able to triumph. The Prophet claimed that these initial victories by the Muslims were due to the direction from Allah and his messengers.

In the days that followed Mohammed's strategic, tactical and spiritual wisdom led to one victory after another for his followers. For this reason, the Muslims were able to consolidate their base of support and the Arab people began to flock to the Prophet's side. Thus the number of believers in Islam continued to swell constantly.

From the very beginning when he first started to preach, Mohammed had shown an unbending determination and commitment to his people. But it was only when he adopted an uncompromising attitude in practical affairs that he began to receive stalwart support from the Arabs and was capable of influencing his society and nation.

If you look closely at the religious and cultural history of Japan and the rest of the world, you can see that individuals who have been able to lead others to true happiness and cause reform of society, have been men with a mission. Their versatility, charisma and ability to touch the souls of their fellow men have made the difference. Divine pronouncements and warnings were not the important factor.

Superior spirits in the divine world are well aware of all this. For that reason they do not want to identify themselves or try to spread a divine message throughout the world. These things are anathema to them, since they consider their mission to be to help men to grow spiritually.

In any event, as you can see, if you are familiar with the fundamental laws of the divine and spirit worlds, then you should be able to immediately spot any "message from an illustrious individual" brought by a spirit as being nothing more than a hoax and the spirit an impostor. Many individuals who have garnered worthless knowledge from the wrong books end up being possessed by these conniving spirits. Of course, spirits posing as superior spirits who offer messages that seem believable and consistent from their contents are most likely very intelligent and knowledgeable former priests, monks or scholars who had become degenerates in life. The young female psychic I referred to earlier no doubt became a victim of one of these shrewd, inferior spirits, who simply toyed with her. Had she been deeply familiar with the spirit and divine worlds and known the fundamentals of *saniwa*, she would have had the willpower to cope with this situation. I must say this was a truly regrettable case.

Two Points About Saniwa

Next so that none of my readers will be taken in by evil spirits, I would like to discuss in a bit more detail the basics of *saniwa* for spiritual pronouncements and divine messages.

The first thing to remember is to look for indications of refinement and vibrancy. Second, the message should be short, with profound meaning in each word. Third, remember that pronouncements or messages made verbally or in book form or jotted down by hand as if by compulsion are definitely phonies. I could name several other indications of bogus articles, but because of space limitations let us leave things with the above.

When we talk about refinement and vibrancy of style in this context, we use a phrase made up of four Chinese characters, pronounced *kiin seido* in Japanese. In olden times in China, this phrase was used when distinguishing the good and bad points of pictures and calligraphy. To put it in a nutshell, if a book or painting has a feel of real life and vividness to it, then it has the kind of refinement and vibrancy we are referring to here.

The same holds true for spiritual or divine messages. The words or Chinese characters chosen should have a superb spirit that pulsates with life and elegance and the messages should ring true when read aloud. They should also reveal an invigorating quality and awe-inspiring authority. Someone who is very familiar with art should immediately be moved by such a message. All of these characteristics should be present with an authentic message. If you are familiar with them, you should easily be able to judge whether the message came from off the top of somebody's head or welled up from deep in the soul of a superior spirit.

Furthermore, physically an inspired work of art or calligraphy should be impressive in its colors and design or the flow of the brush. It should embody formless elegance and reveal the inner artist – in other words the soul of its ultimate creator, a dweller in the spirit world. You can be sure that if the object in question does not display the requisite refinement, vitality and grace, then it is a phony. A true masterpiece, whether in art or literature, will hold fast the attention of anyone familiar with these fields. The principles of the *saniwa* for authenticating messages from the divine and spirit world are the same.

It is much the same as with poetry. Someone who is simply concerned with the rules will not be able to produce a decent poem.

But an inspired poet will sing from the soul and produce tender, flowing, honest sentiments that speak of truth, within the confines of an elegant melody. A poem of genuine quality will move no matter how many times it is read. Even an inspired message from the spirit or divine worlds will have this sense of quality. That is because it is the creation of a superior spirit.

Second, remember too that the more august a high-ranking god or spirit is, the more concise will be his message. But that is true for human writers too. When you are dealing with unsophisticated people, you have to spell things out if you want to get your message across. However, the more educated man has the capacity to digest a great deal of information at a deep level and so must be approached in a different style that can convey profound meanings in terse language, and understand the same as well. Here you are dealing with the type of man who "can hear one thing and understand ten." The kind of person who can understand in the depth of his heart what is happening without anyone having said a word.

The gods and spirits who are sending messages to human beings do not like to say more than is absolutely necessary. So for that reason too, the messages are kept brief. They try to fill the message with spiritual insights and phrases that will capture the mood of the age. The feeling is that the shorter the message, the more profound and more widely applicable will be the nuances it offers.

As I often tell those who attend my seminars, when Japan's gods gather at the Izumo Shrine once yearly, they do not engage in noisy debate or complicated explanations. They sing sacred songs or mull over the enigmatic Zen riddles known as *koan*. Since all of these deities are perfectly familiar with the past, present and future, they have no need to engage in idle discussion.

Oracles

For us to be able to understand the profound inner meanings of the messages that the gods convey to us in their terse messages, we must cultivate the sense of appreciation, and emotional and intellectual sensibility required to ferret out these meanings.

I have repeatedly emphasized the value of true learning and true training. But such things are not acquired overnight. You have to make a total commitment to pay the price in time and effort needed to acquire them. However, one easy method for building up your ability to appreciate things spiritual and divine is "oracle training." What on earth is oracle training?" You might well be saying to yourself. "Is Fukami pulling my leg here?" Such a reaction is understandable considering that I invented this phrase myself. Let me explain it.

Normally with Japanese oracles, at the top of the sheet is written a *waka* poem, below it is a vernacular translation and at the bottom is an explanation of the fortune. A person who is highly endowed with spiritual perception and sensitivity upon reading the first few words of one of these beautiful *waka* poems is likely to burst into tears. For example, "The sun..." alone will conjure up images of the brilliance of the gods, the joy of life, the liveliness of the soul, the rush of ambition, refreshment, a bright existence, freshness, the beginning of anything, release from darkness, the earth bathed in warmth, sparkling hopes, the end of hard times that opens the road to success, and many other things. All of these things might run through the mind and soul of such a person after reading just those two words. He will be able to appreciate the full depth of the divine message contained in that *waka* poem. Needless to say, such people are few and far between.

Most people enjoy only limited spiritual sensitivity and a sense of keen appreciation. That is why they have to read thoroughly the vernacular explanation below the poem. Their sense of appreciation is intellectual, rather than spontaneous understanding from the heart. The bottom level of the oracle sheet contains the simple fortune, which is often nothing but a mix of a bit of wisdom and obvious pandering to the passions and is nearly totally devoid of any higher sense of spiritual appreciation.

Some people will simply be interested in whether they will have good luck or bad. This is the lowest level of knowledge gained from the *omikuji* or oracles. What the "oracle training" I referred to earlier consists of is a conscious effort each time a person reads such an oracle to raise his or her level of understanding, so as to achieve more insight into the divine will.

Do not just be satisfied with knowing whether the oracle signifies good fortune or bad. Always search out the deeper meaning. Read aloud the *waka* poem a bare minimum of ten times and form pictures in your mind of the images that it evokes. Appreciate to the fullest the feelings you have while reading the poem. Never give up and say that you do not understand something or that a particular part is too difficult. If you have to, pretend that you understand. This is important. If you do so, then your soul will be drawn a bit closer to the fathomless divine and spirit worlds and little by little you will be affected by spiritual waves from the gods and spirits and your understanding will grow. This is why I heartily recommend "oracle training."

False Messages From Beyond

Well, I have gone off on another tangent. Let us return to the main discussion.

The third thing to remember is that spoken and written fortunes, those written down in books or even jotted down in one rush by somebody as if a product of direct inspiration at that very moment are all frauds. The *itako* mediums at the Osorezan in northernmost Honshu are very famous for the verbal prophecies. But the spirits that these *itako* act as mediums for are all the spirits of immediate deceased family members or other spirits in the lowest dimension of the spirit world. Never do superior spirits or gods in the divine world speak through these intermediaries.

As I pointed out before, superior spirits and the gods never take possession of some person, so that he or she can spell out their message. They always work slowly on the inner person and reveal their profound message in the most compact fashion possible. They seek to give expression to the message non-verbally through the actions of that person himself.

Just say a false spirit who had taken possession of an individual tried to speak in a terse way resembling a true divine message. Now sooner than the first part had come out than other evil spirits would join the fun spouting occult language, bombast and threats at a feverish pace. Many times the intervention is by an *Inari* fox spirit. If the listener pauses to consider the content of the message and coolly mulls over it for a bit, he will find himself unable to make heads or tails of the whole mess. So the message comes out garbled: "Love, bright light, a new era is coming...." All this is really nothing but malicious mischief on the part of precocious inferior spirits.

Let me give a case of one of my forerunners in the spiritualist field.

I noted earlier that the *itako* at Osorezan usually pass messages from the spirits of dead relatives. But there have been rare cases in Japanese history in which superior spirits and gods of Japan's divine world have called to people directly and communicated to them divine or spiritual messages. The first was Takenouchi no Sukune, who received a message through the deceased empress Jingu. Others appeared later including Onisaburo Deguchi, who is famous in the world of Japanese spiritualism. It was from about his time that the term *saniwa* started to become well known.

Some of these spiritualists had achieved fantastic spiritual powers through long years of training and also enjoyed the protection of powerful gods and spirits. They were able to focus their tremendous spiritual sensitivity and vast knowledge in an instant when they wished to perform *saniwa*. Study of their efforts shows that they ended up dealing mostly with devil *kami* or skillful wicked spirits. Deguchi developed his own special technique for communicating with the gods. It is interesting to note that many of the most prominent spiritualists in Japan in recent decades were followers of Deguchi. Several of them also founded "new religions" in the postwar period.

Deguchi wrote how many people who were interested in developing their psychic powers came to him and asked him to instruct them in his secret technique. However, no matter how rigorously he trained them, his students were inevitably only able to attract spirits commensurate with their own personal character and style of life. Sometimes he thought he had run across an especially promising individual, but in the end things never worked out right. When using his technique, such a person was able to attract a god or spirit, false gods or evil spirits would be right behind. And these people were incapable of fending them off by themselves. The problem is that most of these students lacked sufficient faith. Maybe one out of a hundred would be able to attract a slightly better quality of spirit. But sooner or later that person too would take a wrong tack and end up involved in occultism. Deguchi concluded that it was next to impossible to discover anybody with truly penetrating faith.

Worse than that some of Deguchi's disciples turned on him and began claiming his secret technique for their own and interpreting divine messages as they pleased. All of this thoroughly confused the public. Eventually, the gods and superior spirits had to ask him to stop using the technique. So you can see that even such a remarkable man as Deguchi, who had developed an unparalleled method for communicating with the gods, could not avoid the pitfalls of communicating with the spirit world and the tendency for spiritualism to degenerate in occultism.

You can hardly expect major deities that appear in Japan's native classics of mythology, like the sun goddess Amaterasu Omikami, to communicate with spiritualists who are lacking in the required knowledge and training regarding *saniwa* and who have only had experience dealing with superior spirits. Should they desire to communicate with living people, they would no doubt do so in a ritually clean place through the medium of terse elegant oracles of the most profound kind. Also, since they are well aware that 100% of the so-called divine messages delivered orally are bogus, some good-hearted shamans have stopped trying to give advice to people when it comes to such divine messages.

Even the most ethical and experienced of spiritualists and religious leaders, or rather I should say especially these kinds of people, have stopped trying to pass on any verbal messages from the other world. They realize that the risks and the possibility of interference from evil spirits are simply too great.

I reached that conclusion way back when I was 25 years old. At that time, I decided to avoid the practice and have stuck to my vow ever since then. Over time, I also came to realize that the scribbling down "involuntarily" of divine messages is also a trick. The hand is merely substituted for the mouth. Fundamentally, they are both the same thing. I can name some famous religious leaders in postwar Japan, some even former disciples of Deguchi, who have profited from their alleged ability to transmit messages directly from the gods. Books have even appeared containing samples of the "divine word." Some of these people were very responsible when they were younger. Obviously they have been led astray by clever bands of ruthless spirits. This is clear from the occult content of some of their writings and pronouncements. Despite their earlier accomplishments, they will leave behind a regrettable legacy.

What these people scribble down in the name of a glorious god (but in actuality a manipulating spirit) are most certainly not messages from real gods and superior spirits. I certainly hope that you the reader will not develop interest in such things and thereby be deceived.

When Confused, Rely on Common Sense

It cannot be said that there is no connection between the fact of whether or not a person has interest in spirits and has spiritual characteristics of his own and his ability to discriminate between superior and inferior spirits. In any event, inferior spirits do not particularly care whether or not the person they want to take control of is interested in the spiritual. All they want is to be able to do as they please with his soul, his body and his spirit.

For example, there is the following type of fellow.

Long ago he was an innocent kind of guy. But recently he has been acting wild, scornful of others and totally preoccupied with himself. In the old days he was always trying to improve his character but now he does not really give a damn about things and is content to spend all his days chasing women and getting drunk. He has also become envious of others and is constantly taking the measure of others. He has nothing but contempt for hard work, but is always scheming, trying to find new ways to enjoy himself and make some easy money. When exactly it happened is not clear, but an evil spirit has clearly taken possession of this man's soul.

It is hard to tell in such cases when the possession took place. But most often it occurs after the person has suffered a major failure or setback. At times like these a person is likely to feel hopeless and say, "It's no use. There is nothing but darkness before me. I just don't have the strength to go on living. I might as well just be dead."

When this happens the ancestor spirits that have been tossed into hell, vengeful spirits, location-bound spirits, wandering ghosts and other nasty spirits make an appearance in a jiffy and take possession of the poor guy's flesh. That is to say, when a person gives in to feelings of hopelessness and defeatism, he in effect creates his own pitch black spirit world. Of course no one is going to be bright and cheerful when he feels hopeless and crushed, but the fact is nothing attracts evil spirits more than such a pitch black hopeless spiritual environment. They see the opportunity to control that person's personality.

Still you can take heart, there is a method for protecting yourself from such an onslaught on the part of evil spirits. That is to deal with the worst sense of defeat and hopelessness with firm determination, by at once thinking about the future and substituting despair with a desire for fresh, bright hopes – the will to carve out a new life for yourself. This is the real meaning of faith – the confidence to carry on in the worst of circumstances. And it is exactly this kind of attitude that will get your soul into gear at all times. No matter how evil a spirit might be, no matter how powerful it might be, it will be helpless to possess the soul of a man who is so motivated.

In that case, how do you go about developing such a highly motivated primary soul that is always active? As I explained earlier, the single most important factor is a daily commitment to life and a consciousness of self-established goals. Put simply, that means keeping busy everyday. Of course, included in this activity is constant effort to improve your spiritual self in line with the four approaches we discussed in detail earlier.

Again we are back to the cultivation of true faith through study and training.

Furthermore, when constant thinking about the spirits has your head all muddled and you cannot tell the difference between right and wrong, you need to come back to the world of common sense. After all if you make common sense thinking and proper decorum in the real world your top priorities, you are not going to be bothered by any unwanted "friends" from the spirit world.

Dangerous Half-way Spiritualism

Just for your information, I would like to describe in some detail what happens to a person who develops half-baked psychic powers.

Once a person who had a long string of involvements with various religious organizations paid a visit to our office. Let us call her Ms. A.

Now Ms. A had been making the circuit of various kinds of psychics and spiritualists. As a result, she had acquired a certain degree of occult powers. She also was capable of understanding and experiencing phenomena of the spirit world at a certain level. She had read and apparently been affected by certain of my books, so she came to me asking to undergo a spiritual purification.

I agreed, and undertook the procedures for a normal spiritual purification. Having been around, like I said, she could tell when the spiritual purification took hold and she emotionally shouted, "It's been removed. The spirit's left!"

From that day on that woman always referred to me as her teacher or *sensei*. She was extremely grateful to me. But after I took a little closer look at her past spiritual record, I found I could not share her peace of mind.

What I found was this. Although this woman was married, she

played around constantly with other men and paid absolutely no attention to proper decorum. She was totally blasé about things considered common sense in our everyday world. But at the same time she was obsessed with the gods and spirits. That was because she had once had a very wonderful spiritual experience. Careful observation showed that in many ways she fit the classic model of a middle-aged religious fanatic.

Because the disposition of a person like this – based on such a lifestyle and the personality traits thereby acquired – gives off spiritual vibrations exactly on the wavelength of the lowest level of the spirit world, it should not be any wonder that although this woman constantly sought contact with superior spirits, her spiritual sensibilities were fit for only attracting their inferior counterparts. And they flocked to her, I can guarantee you.

I was worried about many different things in regards to this person, but my anxiety proved well founded.

One day Ms. A, without warning started spreading the word, "Toshu Fukami is possessed. He is possessed by a devil." She started telephoning several members of our group and warning them, "Toshu Fukami is possessed by an evil spirit. Don't go near him."

One person apparently asked her, "Why do you say something like that?"

And she replied, "I have my own special ways of knowing. I was told this. When I first came to the Fukami group, I thought everything was fine. But after a while I started feeling funny. So I am certain that Fukami-*sensei* is possessed by an evil spirit."

Now looking at things objectively, if I suddenly start acting strangely and someone were to say that I have become possessed by an evil spirit, that statement might have some common sense logic to it. But when other people who look at me judge me to be acting normally and it is the person who is making the accusation who is acting strangely, then why on earth should she be saying that I am possessed by a devil?

Good faith common sense would dictate that the person having trouble would look inside herself: "Clearly the reason why you have been acting odd is to be found in some change in the way you are thinking or feeling inside. The question is why?" Then she might humbly ask the gods for help.

In this case, the cause of the problem was simple to ascertain. This woman had been dabbling in the supernatural, issuing warnings to others and making others dependent on her. She had come to think of herself as some kind of great teacher and had become vain, arrogant, egotistic, haughty and so on. Such attitudes attract evil spirits like a magnet. However, the woman had never even realized that she had become so presumptuous.

As a result, if her failings were pointed out to her, she would snap back, "No such thing. You're the one who's been acting strange. I am just fine." In fact she would be very affronted by this whole manner of conversation. In such cases, the person has to be dealt with by someone much more strong-willed or else driven into a real corner. You have to react strongly to such individuals right off the bat. On the other hand, if a normal person developed such a presumptuous attitude, he or she would be likely to stop and think, "I seem to somehow be acting incredibly presumptuous recently. How can I take care of this problem?" This kind of person might have gone a bit astray, but he or she still retains much capacity for self-examination and the virtue of humility.

Sometimes you also encounter people who display "self-deprecating arrogance." On the surface they seem almost servile in their humility, saying for example, "You can't do anything with such an egotistic person as myself, who has a dark karmic heritage and strong emotions. I feel totally unworthy and spiritually immature. It's almost like I'm defiling the rest of you here by intruding on you."

But actually deep inside such people are howling with arrogance, "What rubbish are these idiots spouting? How did I get mixed up with this band of imbeciles? I who have special spiritual power, monetary resources and a long record of spiritual training. You better not treat me lightly, you fools!" Many times people who reek of humility are really walking bundles of unmitigated pride. There are far more of these people than you might realize, too.

As for the case of Ms. A, determined to find out what kind of evil spirit I had been possessed by, she held a nighttime "*saniwa* session" using a chain-rattling device looking something like a high-class ouija board. That is one of the most dangerous things you can do when it comes to attracting evil spirits. It shows that this woman is the type of person who recklessly summons evil spirits, acts presumptuously and engages in all kinds of strange behavior. Such a person is a menace to both herself and others, especially since she can act as a conduit for evil messages.

Such people who get a half-baked initiation into spiritualist secrets often end up like this. How then should Ms. A have responded when she started getting those strange messages from the spirit world?

Well, first of all I would note that she was a perfect example of people who become spiritually confused and divorced from the real world. Before running around talking to other members of our group, she should have first sent me a letter or talked to me directly. If you have some doubts about someone then the best thing first is to confront the person in question with those doubts.

Ms. A might have said to me, "I don't know why it is, but *sensei* you seem to be acting funny recently. I believe you have been possessed by an evil spirit. *Sensei*, please return to your normal self."

She should have used such direct action. Wouldn't you call that an expression of complete sincerity? With such an approach, no matter what spirit may be in possession of a person, for an instant it will certainly loosen its grip on him and the reality will be revealed and can be dealt with. This is surely the way a teacher and disciple should act.

Should you start hearing voices from the spirit world, and getting warnings from there, by all means do not act on them. Doubt them instead, and while continuing to act with proper decorum in our material world, start questioning why this experience is happening to you now and how you should change your thinking. Do so and you will soon be able to properly judge whether these "pronouncements from the spirit world" are genuine or not.

Buddhism Encourages Flexibility

To be honest, human beings are more easily influenced by what is evil than what is good. Temptations weaken resolve, so when evil comes calling, people often lack the willpower and spiritual awareness to just turn it away at the door.

In order for evil to be rejected without question, a person's soul has to be in proper shape. There has to be a mechanism in place that will automatically cause that person to move to the side of good should he be tempted by evil sensations, evil spiritual overtures or evil thoughts.

But in actuality this is very difficult to achieve. Most people who suffer a setback in life are inclined to say "I give up" or "My life is all through." They find it almost impossible to pick themselves up and get back in the race.

However, Buddhism teaches us how to put this self-protecting mechanism in place. Of course, Confucianism, Taoism, Islam and Christianity also do so to an extent. But Buddhism does so in the most profound yet encompassing and detailed way. We might say that it speaks most directly and discretely to the various concerns of the heart and also provides detailed advice on how to recover. Consequently, if you make a sincere, wide-ranging study of Buddhism, you will be able to root out evil sensations and quickly substitute healthy sensations for them, thereby returning to your true nature.

On the other hand, people who become totally preoccupied with the divine world find it difficult to react properly when confronted with evil sensations and temptations; they do not have the right reactive spiritual mechanism inside of them. For that very reason it is extremely difficult to live a life centered solely on the divine world that ignores the physical world we are in.

Incidentally, the Buddha is often pictured sitting on a lotus flower. What exactly does this signify?

As you may know, the root of the beautiful lotus flower is found deep in filthy mud and water. But the beautiful blossom floats serenely above the mire. This muddy water is symbolic of our material world. The flower represents the intricacies of the soul and symbolizes the Buddha world. And what sits above symbolizes several things, including the Buddha himself and the Buddha world hidden in the depths of our hearts that unfolds with enlightenment. In other words, the lotus symbolizes our souls and beings – firmly rooted in the world of men, but with a beautiful flower blooming above which resembles our souls striving towards the divine.

A flower blooming in a field of flowers is of course a beautiful sight. However, it is difficult for something of such beauty and fragility actually to survive and thrive in this filthy, slimy world of ours. That is why the lotus is so important as a symbol. Like the lotus, we must learn to be tough and resilient so we can sink our roots down deep in the material world.

This is the source of the teachings of the Nichiren sect of

Buddhism, which honors the Lotus Sutra as the fount of all wisdom and whose adherents frequently chant *Namu Myoho Rengekyo* ("Glory Be to the Sutra of the Lotus of the Supreme Law!").

Consequently, the study of Buddhism, especially Mahayana Buddhism, develops the required reactive mechanism in the heart. It instills a flexibility that allows a person to react properly when confronted with filthy or evil thoughts and to turn automatically back in the direction of good. Of course, when I refer to "study," I am not talking about a merely cerebral exercise. If the insights gained are not put to practical use, then they are worthless.

As I explained towards the beginning of this book: Thought + Intentions = The Spirit World.

For that reason if you go around willing things bad, such as "Damn it all!" or "To Hell with it!" after you die you are likely to end up becoming a spirit tied to a particular spot, a wandering spirit or a vengeful spirit. Not pretty prospects.

However, through the process of spiritual purification you can counteract these negative thoughts and intentions. And when you do so the inferior spirits that have been in possession of you are free to rise up from the depths of the spirit world.

On the other hand, people who when they were alive had bright, refreshing thoughts have no need to go through a spiritual purification or other form of compensation after they have died. So, if you can learn to control outbursts of negative sentiment, then you will not have to go to a evil part of the spirit world once you leave the material world. No matter what the circumstances, just hang steady and say to yourself: "Hold on here, it won't do to think like that." If you can develop this mechanism of recovery in your soul, you will not have anything to fear when you go to the spirit world.

Environment Is Important

It is Buddhism which provides us with explanations of Nirvana, salvation, and tells us how the human heart should work and the need for emotional flexibility in life. But that is not to say that Buddhism is entirely free from problems. The reason is that this particular religion is too much preoccupied with internal spiritual matters.

As we all know, human beings are not made up of pure spirit; we also consist of flesh and blood. Furthermore, the heart or spirit is also greatly influenced by this physical element. Buddhism is inclined to ignore the physical, or materialistic, aspects of human beings.

Let me be more specific.

For example, let us consider the education of the Crown Prince, Hironomiya when he was a boy. Of course at that time he was in part being trained to become the symbol of the Japanese nation. His education was designed with this goal in mind. From the time he was a little infant, he was raised in a very good environment. I do not think that he was plagued very often by problems with bad thoughts or bad intentions.

But what about the case of a person who is born into a very poor environment, the opposite of what the Crown Prince enjoyed as a boy? No matter how much he may try, it will be very difficult for such an individual to concentrate on good thoughts. Such a person stands in the greatest need of Buddhism for support.

What I am saying is that before getting fixated on talking about training or cultivating the soul, we first have to look at what kind of environment is required to produce a beautiful soul. This is the most important thing to bear in mind. The creation of a proper environment from a young age is vital. As the saying "Well fed, well bred" makes clear, if we can attain a certain degree of comfort in the material world, then we will be less prone to evil intentions.

So, in other words, our heart and our thoughts are not everything. If the material circumstances in which we live are good, then we will tend to have virtuous hearts. And we will also be able to develop superior sensibilities and enviable spirituality.

That is the reason why I say Buddhist devotees who shelve problems related to improving the material world and society and become preoccupied with their souls and their thinking are making a serious mistake.

Confucianism: the Road to Harmony

Well then, what is the proper road to reform in this material world. It is provided by the teachings of the Chinese sage Confucius. In other words, it is Confucianism.

What makes these teachings so relevant to the real world we live in are the virtues that Confucius sought to instill in men, namely: benevolence, righteousness, etiquette, sagacity and sincerity. Let us take a look at the virtue of etiquette, or propriety.

Confucius spoke of the need to "control the self and return to etiquette." By this he did not simply mean that people need to learn how to bear up under their hardships. No, he was saying that we must deny the passions that are eating at our souls if we wish to return to the correct path of Heaven and Nature and become fulfilled persons. This is accomplished through reliance on etiquette or proper decorum.

But what exactly is this etiquette or decorum that I am referring to here? It is beautiful harmony between the natural order and human society.

Let us take the example of a marriage ceremony. It is said that these days many couples choose not to go through a formal wedding ceremony. If conditions so warrant or the couple is in complete agreement on this point, then there is really nothing wrong with such a decision. But I think the average couple still wants to go through the ceremony so that they might share their happiness with others. This attitude reflects the true spirit of "etiquette."

Funerals are another good example. You hear people saying all kinds of things on this score. For example: "Everyone is going to die in the end, so there is no need to hold a special funeral ceremony. It's enough to do like some people do in the United States, have your ashes scattered from an airplane."

Nevertheless, it really is appropriate to have a formal funeral ceremony at which a Buddhist priest reads from the sutras as a kind of last send-off for the deceased. The condolences rendered by the deceased relatives and friends and their reminiscing bring home to the person the fact that he or she is dead. During the ceremony relatives and friends also have an opportunity to deepen tender recollections of the dead person and to offer a kind of compensation for all the favors they received from that person when he or she was still alive.

It must be admitted, however, that there are occasions when ceremonies are held merely for their own sake. This is not etiquette, but an evil abuse or travesty of true etiquette. A ceremony does not reflect true etiquette unless the spirit is pure and the feelings shown come straight from the heart.

The essence of etiquette is as I mentioned earlier an ability to achieve beauty through harmony with society and development of proper order, a mature expression of true human feelings, and in a broader sense, through the establishment of harmony with Heaven and Nature. Etiquette is merely the system of rules that makes all this possible. When you look at things from this standpoint, the maintenance of a proper balance through the use of etiquette and decorum is highly useful in keeping us on the correct path in our material world.

The Big Three

Let me review a bit what we have learned in Chapter 1.

As I reiterated several times, if you do not wish to lose to the evil spirits, you should concentrate on acquiring three things: true learning, training – to include familiarity with the arts and a strong faith.

Well, what then is true faith? It is not just believing in and worshipping the gods. That is merely religious belief, which is different from faith.

No, what I mean by true faith is based on real learning and training of the soul. Why are human beings born onto the face of our planet? What is good; what is evil? Unless you grasp the true answers to such questions and live a proper human life in accordance with the wishes of the gods, you cannot say that you possess true faith.

However, if you do develop real faith rooted in true learning and self-cultivation, even should evil spirits threaten to take possession of you, because your soul will give off a special spiritual glow, you will be able to escape the danger. Of course you will also receive considerable direction from your guardian spirits. For that reason, even when it seems that you are going to be defeated, you will be able to continue with confidence in the correct direction.

On the other hand, if you do not acquire true faith, are fascinated with the spirit world where the evil spirits dwell and faith healing or other psychic powers bestowed from above, or exhibit rampant egotism, conceit and presumptuousness, then you are in great danger of becoming possessed by an evil spirit. You are especially vulnerable at times when your character is teetering, such as at the moment of a major setback or defeat.

On the other hand, another such time of maximum vulnerability is when there is a changing of the guard among a person's guardian spirits. I have explained this in several of my previous books, but let me just note here that any drastic change in a person's environment which results in his setting out on a new course, through a reorientation of his *mitama*, usually also results in a change of his guardian spirits, with a higher class band replacing one that is their inferior.

That happens, for example, when a student is taking his entrance exams for high school or university and must buckle down to do the very best job he is capable of. (I should point out that the entrance exam is an ordeal that can decide a person's entire future in Japan.) Or let us give a business situation: a businessman has suffered a major setback and he has to draw on all his fighting spirit to stage a comeback. In such instances, powerful guardian spirits will replace the person's normal companions, so that the spirit world can give him the best possible back-up.

In other words, when an individual's personal environment changes greatly, the spirit lineup behind him also is likely to change. However, whether the spirits that step in to take charge of his fate are good or evil depends on his own situation at the time – what his thoughts and disposition or spirit are like at that particular point in time.

If the person is saying to himself, "I give up" or "I might as well be dead" or "I'll get that bastard," he is already easy prey for the evil spirits.

But if he is thinking along the following lines, "O.K., let's hang in there" or "Things are tough, but I'll never give up" or "It makes my blood boil, but I'll just forgive and forget; I'll be a better man for it," then you can be sure that person's guardian gods and spirits are going to take good care of him.

An instant where a person faces a fundamental crisis, when he feels his whole personality is in danger of collapsing and that he is losing control of his very self is meant as a test from the gods to see whether he will turn towards good or evil. Some people will be destroyed by such a crisis, others will slough off their old selves and become better individuals. These experiences should be regarded as watersheds that decide whether the person in question will henceforth enjoy good luck or encounter disasters.

People who do not handle these watershed crises well become an easy target for possession by evil spirits. In fact this kind of person always seems to be under the spell of an evil spirit or an ill-intentioned ancestor spirit. He is something like a "base camp" for the evil spirits, a blotter that just soaks up wandering spirits.

Such being the case, it is not a matter of undergoing or not a spiritual purification. But even should he undergo a spiritual purification, because he will continue to be like a blotter, nothing will fundamentally change.

However, if a person is determined to do whatever it takes to cut his relations with evil spirits, then to do so he must be prepared to change his character completely. If he is willing to make such a major commitment, then after a spiritual purification he should be able to start enjoying such good fortune that you would think it belonged to a totally different person. Of course, it is easy to speak but difficult to do. Even if a person understands what he needs to do, more often than not he finds it very difficult to take the necessary action. That is why I established the organization World Mate, which carries out seminars and various other activities designed to help people make themselves better. It offers guidance that will allow even a person beset with a multitude of problems to make astounding progress over time. Naturally membership does not depend on whether a person has undergone a spiritual purification or not.

Incidentally, spirits make contact with human beings in various ways, but we human beings – creatures of flesh and blood that we are – are not meant to be manipulated by them. We should be concentrating on ourselves and limiting our involvement with them to getting rid of evil spirits or inviting friendly spirits to back us up.

For that reason, a human being should make the world of his own heart and soul the center of his life. It is important to establish a right pattern of healthy living and to maintain that condition by self-oriented activity that maintains a balance between concerns for the material world and the divine world – a world of good sensations. If he does not do so, then his entire life will end up being manipulated by spirits. Instead, a person should strive to keep one up on the hostile spirits, while using assistance from good spirits in his quest to make use of the truth.

Up till now clairvoyants and other psychics have concerned themselves only with the spirit world, people of religion only with the gods, and common sense individuals only with the mundane affairs of our everyday world. Each followed his own path.

But such tunnel vision is a big mistake. The reason why is that each type of person can only see one of the three worlds: the spirit world, divine world or material world. The correct approach to life is to bear all three worlds in mind while trying to become the best person you can and seeking to bring happiness to those around you.

If you concentrate solely on the spirits, you are going to be taken advantage of by evil spirits. If you think only about our material world, you are not going to receive supernatural help from the gods and Buddhas and so therefore will not enjoy Heaven-sent good fortune. If you are preoccupied with the divine world, you are not going to be able to put roots down in human society and will suffer from a lack of social intercourse.

At the beginning of time, the Supreme Creator of the Universe made Heaven and Earth and the three worlds – divine, spiritual and material. So if we would understand God correctly, we must simultaneously respect all three worlds and seek to achieve a healthy balance in our perspectives on them.

Furthermore, we must constantly work to improve our own *mitama* spirits, make our primary soul glow with spirituality and do good for those around us. If we are able to do all this, then we will be living a proper human life. Remember even if you say you believe in the gods, that alone does not constitute true faith. Far from it. In fact if you lull yourself into a sense of false safety through such thinking, you may be setting yourself up for possession by some evil spirit. Think about this point very carefully.

CHAPTER 2

How To Beat the Evil Spirits

Concentrate to Erase Your Troubles

Why do people become possessed by evil spirits? If you understand the reasons why, you will be in a position to develop suitable defensive strategies. I think I made this point more than amply clear in Chapter 1. But to understand something intellectually and to feel it in your very bones are two very different things. Therefore, in this chapter I would like to address this question in more detail, from a wider perspective, and perhaps in more interesting fashion.

First of all, let me note that evil spirits like to go after the kind of soul that we might call "empty." So if your heart and soul are filled with suitable feelings at all times, you stand in little danger of becoming one of their targets.

For example, one of the most effective measures for keeping evil spirits at arm's length is always to have goals in your daily life and constantly work to achieve those goals.

If you have firmly established in your mind how you will live each day, each week, each month, each year, indeed your entire life, or what you will strive for in your career, and then you do your level best to follow that game plan, evil spirits will be able to discover no chinks in your armor and consequently will not be able to possess you. They will just melt away.

In Japanese we have a saying that is a rough equivalent of: "An idle brain is the devil's workshop." This means that too much time on one's hands is not good in a spiritual sense. There is also the connotation that a person who cannot make good use of whatever free time comes his or her way cannot amount to much. In terms of the spirit dimension, what it really means is that those who are prone to evil conduct have left gaps in their hearts through which evil spirits have gained entrance.

On the other hand, people who with their own volition establish clear goals and then advance towards them, not only will not have any gaps in their heart, their souls will shine brightly with virtue.

Naturally, this luster cannot be perceived by the human eye. But the denizens of the spiritual world, in other words good and evil spirits, as well as individuals who truly possess psychic powers, can clearly see this spiritual aura. In fact, if he is aware of the phenomenon, even the average person can indirectly sense this presence through the body language of such a virtuous person. That person's eyes will have a special shine to them. His manner of speech will seem somehow specially animated. His entire person will give off an energy force. There are many such indications. The fact is that this shining candle flame of the soul is clear evidence that the person's guardian spirits are backing him up totally. They are really joining their own brilliance to his, thus making his spiritual flame burn all the brighter.

Inferior spirits and outright wicked spirits are unable to approach near these majestic flames. Even if they should try, they will grow dizzy and weak before its dazzling brilliance. On top of that, the guardian spirits that hover around the person and serve as his bodyguards will rush forward to his defense and with intimidating cries of "Be gone," they will send the interlopers packing.

By the way, I recall a case in which a young woman asked for help from a Zen priest in the following manner, "I am troubled by all kinds of problems and worries, my soul is in so much turmoil that I cannot do my job properly. What can I do so that I can concentrate on my work?"

The priest answered as follows, "Oh, is that so? I can see how you would be troubled. But it is really not a cause for worry. Just get so involved in your job that you won't have time to fix your mind on your problems. If you do that, I think you'll see that everything will work out right."

People naturally tend to think that if they are plagued by personal worries they cannot work. But that is not true at all. For one thing, you will not find a person on the face of the earth who does not have his or her own problems. But all we can do is to keep on trying to struggle forward. So we have to force ourselves to stand up and squarely face our problems. These very troubles and worries serve as a stimulus to make us better human beings. The problem is that when people have too much free time, these same troubles and worries can overwhelm them. They spend their time mulling non-constructively over their vexations, which only makes things worse. In fact, on their own they generally end up creating new problems to go with the old.

Take for example people who suffer from insomnia. "I want to sleep, and I get into bed ready to sleep, but sleep just won't come." That is certainly a common complaint. But the fact is that with the exception of cases clearly due to medical problems, insomnia is largely attributable to the fact that the person in question is simply not physically tired enough to sleep.

If you think back to when you were a child, I am sure you will admit that you would often fall asleep after wearing yourself out at play – sometimes even when you were eating. Or maybe you have had occasion to work late at night three days in a row. By the fourth day you are ready to sleep like the dead. So in short, while we are on earth the best thing to do is throw ourselves entirely into something, thereby keeping ourselves as busy as possible. Do that and you will find that the solutions to your problems seem to pop into your head right out of nowhere, maybe even while you are just walking. If you are in that constructive state of mind, free time will become a real pleasure, since it will be an integrated part of your overall lifestyle.

As for the average housewife who does not venture out into the employment market, the trick is for her to devote herself wholeheartedly to all her daily tasks, including cleaning around the house and doing the laundry. If she acts with body and soul in perfect unison, her guardian spirits will answer the various requests that she makes. This is a secret method for resolving problems.

And as a result, vexations and quandaries will disappear naturally.

Furthermore, those who do give their utmost in this manner, but who do not even notice that their prayers are being answered or that they have unconsciously developed a most successful strategy for coping with life, will receive increasing support by the day from their guardian spirits. As a result, their once seemingly insoluble problems will gradually melt away. In this way, even if people have anxieties and difficulties in life, they find that they can bounce back and overcome the uneasiness and worries that trouble them so.

We might define hope as "happiness busy at work." And if we give our all every moment we are alive, we are certain to find the path that is best for us clearly visible before us. This style of living will without fail attract good spirits and good fortune. This might all seem very straightforward and self-evident, but the fact is that it is extremely difficult to live this way conscientiously in real life.

The Path of Kusunoki Masashige

If you live only for the moment, doing your best ever single moment while maintaining a forward-looking attitude, you will find that you no longer have time to think about those things that previously got on your nerves or bothered you. And once your worry is gone, then the clouds of bewilderment and anxiety that had been hanging low over you, will miraculously evaporate. In this regard, I would like to relate a true episode from Japanese history.

It concerns the final fight of the famous 14th century royalist hero Kusunoki Masashige at the battle of Minatogawa in 1336.

As I explained in *Divine Powers*, Masashige had incredible psychic powers. He therefore knew that the shogun Ashikaga Takauji, who was opposing Emperor Go-Daigo, planned to march with a great host on the then capital, Kyoto. The Emperor and his principal advisors held a war council at which Kusunoki reportedly counseled that it would be best to allow Takauji and his rebel army into the capital and then when they had let their guard down to launch an all-out attack on them.

Specifically, he advised Go-Daigo to take refuge on nearby Mt. Hiei. In the meantime, he and the main guard royalist forces would advance up the Yodo River and pounce on Takauji's forces when the time seemed ripe. He guaranteed victory if his plan was followed.

However, Go-Daigo's other right-hand men, many of whom were court nobles inexperienced in war, quickly attacked this highly viable strategy. They declared it out of the question that the emperor should flee and hide from rebels. The enemy should be met in battle and destroyed, they argued. Masashige could only reply that such an approach would result in certain defeat.

However, the war council's decision went contrary to Masashige's advice. Masashige was well aware that it was his duty to give his all to implement any decision approved by the emperor. So despite his misgivings, he tranquilly set off for battle.

As Masashige had foreseen, the imperial forces were decimated at the Battle of Minatogawa. And the hero and master strategist Masashige lost his own life in most gallant fashion. After that defeat, however, another loyalist general Nitta Yoshisada used the strategy proposed by Masashige to great effect and scored several outstanding victories as a result. If Masashige had been allowed to implement his strategy in the first place, the course of Japanese history might have been fundamentally altered, since after Go-Daigo no Japanese emperor ever has held real power.

Because Go-Daigo and his advisors turned down a highly practical plan for reasons of "face," perhaps the greatest bulwark of the Throne was lost forever. Masashige's heart must have been filled with very complicated feelings when he decided to march to certain death at Minatogawa.

Because of his strategic sense and his psychic powers, the loyal vassal knew that he stood absolutely no chance of surviving the encounter. It was an objective "fact" as far as he was concerned.

Naturally, considering the circumstances it was difficult for Masashige to face death with total equanimity. Too many worries were preying on his mind. He knew his responsibility and duty as an imperial retainer. But at the same time before the battle even commenced, he knew that defeat and death were his inevitable lot. Still, he went proudly to the battlefield, despite the resentment in his heart. As a knowledgeable commander, he could only decry the waste of life and lost chance. His soul must have been in turmoil.

On his way to the field of Minatogawa, Masashige encountered a locally renowned Zen priest by the name of Minki Soshun.

Masashige asked him how he should react when he reached the border between life and death. Minki Soshun replied to the effect that the artificial barrier separating the world of the living from the otherworld should be severed with one quick blow from a sword. The sword in question is actually the sword of spiritual awakening to the meaning of the illusion we call life. In other words, the bonze was telling Masashige that the correct way to face all in life or death was by accepting them as Heaven's will - spiritual tests given us by the divine world.

When Masashige asked if he severed the twin heads of life and death where would they fall, Minki Soshun roared, "Kaa! Here! This very place. It is your entire being. Transcend all divisions and illusions and discover the ultimate truth in yourself!"

The priest let out the cry "kaa!" in a very mournful tone. After hearing this strange reply to his question, Masashige, who was clad in armor, rose to his feet and after shaking his head up and down several times, serenely said to the priest,

"Bonze. I truly thank you for what you have told me. If Kusunoki Masashige had not met this priest here today and received his instruction, all the ideals and faith that he had acquired during his lifetime would have been for naught in the end. I am deeply indebted to you."

What had happened here was that as soon as Masashige apprehended the meaning of the priest's words, the clouds of apprehension that had been dogging him disappeared in an instant. Not a shadow remained in his heart and he could offer his entire being to the battle without the slightest tinge of regret. Life or death – in the end they were equally irrelevant. All that Masashige could do was to wholeheartedly submit himself to the will of Heaven and fight his best until his last breath. Indeed during the Battle of Minatogawa although Masashige received 13 serious sword wounds, his indomitable will kept him fighting on. Then when there was no more hope whatsoever, he committed ritual *seppuku* suicide.

Masashige's spirit and pure lifestyle did not die with him, however. His son Kusunoki Masayuki carried on in his place. After Ashikaga Takauji set up a rival court, the so-called Northern Court, the legitimate Imperial line, the Southern Court, continued to fight for an Imperial Restoration. Its adherents were infected by the loyal spirit of Masashige and loyalty to one's sovereign was the ultimate raison d'être of a government minister. The chronicles of that war-wracked period make clear that many of the partisans of the Southern Court were living proof of this philosophy.

Centuries later under the Tokugawa Shogunate, Tokugawa Mitsukuni (1628-1700), who was the head of the Mito branch of the family and in effect a vice-shogun, began the compilation of the *Dai Nihon Shi*, the first comprehensive history of Japan. In the draft portion on the Nambokucho Period Masashige is praised as a paragon of courage and loyalty. So impressed by Masashige was Mitsukuni that he ordered a monument to be erected on the great general's grave bearing the tribute that he wrote, "Here lies the loyalist of ministers, Kusunoki." His motivation was obviously the desire to see as many people as possible recognize his unsurpassed fidelity to his emperor, based on his deep wisdom, benevolence and courage, as well as his sense of filial piety and sincerity. You can still see that monument today at the Minatogawa Shrine in Kobe City in western Japan.

Then too there was Yoshida Shoin, one of the most important ideological shapers of the Meiji Restoration of 1867. He kept a picture of Masashige on his wall and issued a manifesto to his students at the private academy that he ran, many of whom went on to become leaders of the new Japan, declaring that they should learn from the example of Masashige.

The aphorism that the priest told Masashige on his final journey to Minatogawa became beloved by many of the greatest men in Japanese history who followed in the great general's spiritual footsteps and sought to honor him by its use. It also served to provide them spiritual comfort when they faced their own darkest hours. We human beings must all face quandaries and problems. But some of Japan's best and brightest learned that they could sweep these obstructions from their path by adopting this philosophy. In other words, they saw that the way to freedom is to face squarely the destiny that Heaven has decided is yours and to do your utmost no matter what the chances of success or failure.

Know Yourself Before Dealing With Others

I remember a woman whom I once counseled. She went on and on, "I can't do this...That's out of the question too... That too...Be it this, or be it that, I'm always in a quandary as for what to do."

Even though it is a fact that if a person bravely faces the present reality and does the best that he or she can, perplexities and problems will disappear and spiritual impediments will dissolve, some people are unaware of this fact and stay embroiled in their troubles, while they go around from here to there asking others for advice.

There are many kinds of fortune-telling: Shinto style, onomancy, palmistry and astrology – just to name a few. Usually the kind of person who consults with fortune-tellers frequently has a lot of time on his or her hands. Please don't get me wrong: consulting a fortune-teller is perfectly all right. But if a person runs to a fortune-teller for a consultation every time a problem crops up in his life, that is not at all good. He will end up relying entirely on someone else and unable to handle his or her own affairs. Furthermore, he will lose chances to be tested and to build his courage by grappling with and overcoming small difficulties in life. It is usually the person who is willing to face his destiny square on and not look too far down the road who ends up enjoying good fortune.

In this regard, I must admit that I myself tell fortunes, using my special spiritual powers. With these I can judge the fate of the people who come to see me. However, I refuse to give any more consultations after I have enlightened them concerning one or two major things in their lives.

I welcome the kind of person who thinks out the problem as far as he can before coming to see me. But I do not care for the kind of individual who comes running to me every time a little rain falls into his life. The reason is that if a person is always asking for assistance, he or she will never be in the position to help others.

If you think about it in terms of the business world, you cannot deny that repeat orders are the base of a company's stable income. So naturally they are highly welcome. But I do not tell fortunes to make money. I am solely concerned about the future welfare of the people who turn to me for help.

If a person tries everything possible, but still cannot work out a solution to his problems, then before turning to other people for assistance, he should first ask the help of his guardian gods and guardian spirits with all the sincerity at his command and look to them for counsel. If he does so, I can guarantee that someone will tell him the correct thing to do, or he will get a flash of inspiration. Regardless of how it comes about, he will find the correct solution to what is troubling him.

Nevertheless, let me just caution you once again that it is dangerous to rely solely on direct spiritual contact with your guardian spirits.

As I explained in some detail in Chapter 1, direct spiritual messages and inspirations can play tricks on you. Even if the first one or two are correct, inevitably the third or fourth will turn out to be a false message from an evil spirit. It will end up causing you great embarrassment or failure. That is 100 percent guaranteed. If a person tries to tell another person the "message" from his guardian spirit, you know what will happen? Maybe the first couple of words will be O.K., but by the time he gets to the third word I guarantee you the hex will be on and you will be mouthing the thoughts not of your guardian spirit but of a totally different spirit – a spiritual meanie who is out to make an ass of you. I promise you that is exactly what will happen. So be careful about entreating your guardian spirits too often.

Incidentally, recently a rather unusual phenomenon has been manifesting itself: young, spiritually acute businessmen. I understand that when these men want to get down to work, they often suddenly feel that something is wrong with them physically. Their superiors might get angry at them and accuse them of being "soft," but such scolding does not do the least bit of good. I would advise that in such cases the person be taken off desk work for a while and allowed to do something where he can move around a bit.

No attention should be paid even if the young worker feels terrible and vomits a bit. Let him feel awful; let him vomit. The main thing is to keep him moving.

The suffering worker for his part should resolve not to think in such cases that the cause of the malady is interference from an evil spirit. For the instant he does so, he will be under the control of that evil spirit.

Should he be plagued by nausea or headaches, he should take some stomach medicine or pain killers. That is because the very act of doing so will reinforce in his consciousness the idea that the cause of the problem is physical, and by no means any kind of interference from the spirit world.

Act in this fashion, constantly thinking in terms of the material world, and you will find that the debilitating condition will naturally clear up on its own and your guardian spirits will rush in to replace any evil spirit lurking around, looking to do you harm. As I explained elsewhere, these guardian spirits are always willing to back up people who are willing to help themselves. The most important thing is for you to make actual efforts yourself.

The way to eliminate interference from evil spirits or unwanted spirits of any kind is to have a thorough change of heart and spirit. This is absolutely vital. The secret to doing this is by "switching channels" from the one tuned to the spirit world to the one tuned to our material world.

By the way, you will often find situations like the following in office life:

A manager may have a subordinate whose work habits and attitude towards his job is less than exemplary. And he even might conclude that for the sake of his other hard working employees he should try to find a way to get rid of this bad egg. But if he takes up the problems one after the other with the fellow in question, he is likely to get nowhere.

If you say, "Your attitude on the job is poor and you haven't been delivering in your work..."

He is likely to argue back, "Well, your results aren't all that great either, are they?"

"Well you may have a point there, but you've been late to work on countless occasions, and..."

"Now man, you're one to be talking about being late. Didn't I see you sneak in here late just last week?"

In such a case, you will not be able to accomplish anything by such a direct approach. After all, a person with this kind of attitude is hardly going to be fazed by a simple scolding. In fact, his "don't give a damn" attitude is the reason why he acts the way he does.

If you really want to get rid of the creep, make it clear that he has absolutely no value to the company – in other words make him feel like the zero that he is.

So make up a *sayonara* scenario something like the following:

"Since you've worked so hard, we've prepared a special desk for you. The desk you've been using up till now doesn't give you enough sunlight. So from today we're going to put you over near this window. I'll take care of the work you've been handling up to now. We've got a project we want you to bring all you're concentration to: pasting postage stamps on the office mail."

(It should be noted that workers in Japan who are over the hill or considered superfluous for any reason are often seated near the window. There is even a special name for them: the *madogiwazoku*, which literally means "the window seat tribe.")

Now back to the case of our troubling colleague. Another way to signal him the message that he is no longer wanted around is to ignore the work he is doing.

For example, if he comes to ask you a question, just tell him you are busy and that he should come some other time. Or you might put him off by saying, "I really don't have a clue. You just try figuring it out yourself please."

In most cases, you can expect to see the guy's letter of resignation on your desk in no time at all. The kind of undesirable people that we are talking about here are usually sophists, who will talk your head off without saying anything of value. So it is nothing but a waste of time to let them run on and on. If a person of this type causes a real scandal or blatantly and repeatedly transgresses company regulations, then it is easy enough to just get rid of him despite the fact that most major Japanese companies honor the tradition of lifetime employment. But sometimes you get the kind of employee who does his assigned job, but whose presence is overall a minus for the company; he can cause real headaches for his superiors, since he is so hard to get rid of. And I am sure that in such nasty cases the vast majority of managers would do exactly as I have suggested.

In any event, let's summarize the appropriate strategy. The most important thing is to ignore the malcontent's existence – give him the silent treatment. Do so and the little sophist will see his game lose its appeal since he has no partner to talk in circles with or purposely upset. Staying where he is will thus lose its significance in his own mind.

It is much the same strategy you would follow in getting rid of an evil spirit.

Since evil spirits previously were human beings, naturally they have emotions similar to those of living people. If people ignore them, they react no differently than a person – our unwanted employee for example – would in the same situation.

If you make it impossible for an evil spirit to take possession of people and cause them grief, do you know what happens? It is filled with horror and just up and slips away.

Incidentally, the city news pages of your daily newspaper or the TV news are filled with a lot of tragic and violent stories. Many of these tragedies take place when people involved are in a psychologically abnormal state.

There have been numerous incidents in which a person goes "mad" and attacks and maybe even kills a complete stranger. When asked why he did what he did, the assailant will frequently confess in bewildered fashion, "There was this voice telling me that unless I got that guy first, he was going to kill me. I didn't even realize what I was doing. That voice forced me into action."

Ask psychiatrists about such cases and they will tell you, "These are classic cases of schizophrenia in which the person is absolutely convinced that there is another person or persons inside himself."

Despite that fact, if a competent psychic sees something like this, he or she immediately can detect in that voice the presence of an evil spirit. In other words, we know that an evil spirit has taken possession of the individual and is merrily going about doing the dirty things that evil spirits are wont to do.

The way to prevent these evil spirits from doing what they want to do is the same as I described earlier. In other words, even if you are fully aware of the presence of the evil spirit bent on doing you harm, try to ignore its presence, its constant whispering and its efforts to make you spiritually unhappy, and just go about your own proper business.

Concentrate on the Immediate

Of course, if you are actually involved in such a situation, it is far from easy to ignore the presence of the evil spirits. When it comes to fellow human beings, we can verify their existence with our eyes. But spirits are invisible, so they usually take possession of a person before that person is even aware that they are around. Furthermore, people who have the characteristics of a spiritualist often find it difficult to ignore these pesky spirits.

Let me describe a specific case that illustrates these points.

"Ah! It's got to be a fox spirit that has taken possession of me. Either a fox with a human spirit or an *Inari* shrine fox. Come to think of it uncle used to frequent *Inari* shrines, so it has to be an *Inari* fox that has merged into a human soul. What can I do? How can I get rid of this awful spirit. There has to be some appropriate sutra I can chant."

You often find people like this busily chanting their sutras; but all to no avail. In fact the effort is counterproductive. The more a person like this tries to get rid of the fox spirit, the more that evil being will gain control of his consciousness. And since the soul and spirit will become more closely fused as a result of the exercise, the evil spirit will find it even easier to take possession of the person. Thus the effort to discipline the rowdy spirit will end up boomeranging.

I expect that some of my readers might be tempted to succumb to the following thinking: "Oh, so an evil spirit is lurking around, is it? That's not going to have any influence on me. I won't pay the least bit of attention to the brat."

Such a blasé attitude is liable to backfire, however. Because if you simply try to ignore the existence of something that is actually there, you will be leaving chinks in your armor so that the evil spirit can get inside you.

You must realize that if you either try to fight these spirits head on or completely ignore them, you will end up on the same spiritual plane as them, fighting in an arena of their choice.

What then is a sensible strategy? As I explained earlier, what you need to do is choose an entirely different field of battle here in the material world into which you can pour your entire energy and concentration. It can be your work, artistic endeavors, or whatever. The important thing is to become totally absorbed in affairs of this material dimension and to let go spontaneously of any preoccupation with the Fourth Dimension - the spiritual world. Determination to forget completely about the Fourth Dimension is what is called for. This is the most important thing to keep in mind. If you do so, then the evil spirits will find themselves stuck in their own arena with no foe to contend with. As a result, they will become impotent to trouble you. This is the real meaning of my advice to change your spiritual outlook and ignore the existence of the spirits.

I would note that my own spirituality is highly sensitive. So I am the type of person who is very easily susceptible to interference from the spirit world. As a result, there have been times when I suffered greatly from evil spirits who attacked and tried to take control of my soul. I was set on by these evil spirits around the clock. I felt like vomiting; my eyes became bloodshot; and I otherwise suffered beyond description.

On such occasions, I responded by becoming even more engrossed in the book I was writing at the time, practiced calligraphy to concentrate the mind, drew pictures, played the flute, gulped down some fried noodles, or performed some other action on which I could totally concentrate. In my case, if we were to perform a spiritual purification every time evil spirits came around, I would be performing these rites every single day. That is how incredibly sensitive I am to approaches from the spirit world.

Besides doing everything possible to block thoughts of the spirit world from my mind, I rely on the gods and my guardian spirits for help in meeting the challenge. And they do provide me great strength and comfort. And they will do the same for anyone who prays to them. For that reason the evil spirits cannot sink their poisonous fangs into me and I can pass my days in peace.

I would also note that as individuals progress in this process for dealing with the evil spirits they become better people as a result, and this in turn becomes manifested in a better reputation and ability to operate in society.

Sad Fate of Spiritualists

Since I referred to people who have highly developed spiritual personalities and are therefore easily subject to interference from the spirit world, I would like to touch a little bit more on how these types of individuals interact with the spirits.

The type of spiritualist who is constantly engaged in a test of wills with the spirits is really only taking half advantage of his or her psychic powers. Actually, you might say that it is a sad fate to be "blessed" with such psychic powers. Of course, if such a person uses these psychic powers to draw on the strength of the gods and acquire real power in the material world in conformance with the will of the gods and common sense, then he or she will know how to respond properly to interference from the spirits. The problem is when people only do things half right. Then involvement with the spirit world can prove a trap from which a person like this will find it difficult to escape. This unfortunate situation is really quite understandable, however, precisely because such a person can see and hear the spirits in question, he or she is more likely to be tempted to try to get rid of them.

But there is something I should caution you about in this regard. Do not forget that in all circumstances such a person should see most beautiful things, visualize most beautiful worlds.

Naturally, for psychics battle with the evil spirits is an everyday affair. Always they have to struggle with inferior spirits – the kind that haunt the lowest depths of hell.

I would like you to imagine for a moment what these inferior spirits look like. Look at them once and you will never want to look at them again....no, it is even worse than that. Even though their eyes jut out, their noses are crushed and they lack hands and feet, these nasty spirits get around quite easily and display fantastic strength. They have strange voices and ghoulish forms and clothing. Worms, centipedes, maggots and spiders cover their bodies and squirm about. Sometimes they have forms somewhat resembling human beings. At other times they look like giant snakes, sporting horns and fangs. And they give off a strange, offensive odor. They are so incredibly ugly that it is difficult to even gaze at them. The monsters we see on television and in the movies are beauties compared to these creatures.

What do you think happens if a person has to look at such grotesque monstrosities every single day? Well the natural result is that no matter who you are you are bound to develop eyes with a strange expression in them.

That is the reason for the odd-looking eyes and poor physiognomy of many psychics. You find many of them addicted to wearing sunglasses. In fact about the only psychic who has cool, welcoming eyes and a pleasant cast to his features is I myself, Toshu Fukami! Well, maybe I am exaggerating. To say such a thing is certainly a bit immodest. But the truth is that no matter how filled with the spirit of benevolence and the desire to help others a psychic might be, constant exposure to what goes on in hell is bound to affect adversely the look in a person's eyes and his looks.

For the same reason quite a few policeman leave something to be desired when it comes to their eyes and other facets of their looks. You are bound to be affected if you deal with the worst in society.

It goes without saying, that the job of a policeman is to catch criminals. If a criminal tries to run away, then the police have to go in pursuit. In such an instance, the blood pounds through the veins of the policemen just like it does for the criminal. As a result, the police also developed a jaundiced attitude. After all, you do not find many policemen laughing as they pursue a dangerous criminal, do you?

Of course, the police are good people. But when they are on the job, they have to adopt such an attitude. We should thank them for bearing up with this load.

Actually, such glaring eyes or intimidating looks cause no major problems. Where you encounter trouble is when a person's way of thinking is also affected for the worse.

If a person is always forced to look at ugly, dirty things, his or her soul will almost inevitably become somewhat ugly as a result. Unfortunately, the hearts of psychics who have to look upon low-class spirits every day cannot help but become warped to a certain extent.

This situation is a definite pitfall for psychics who are unable to look beyond the spirit world. What they need to do is get to know the divine world as well, while living to the fullest in their real home – the material world. If they do this and develop an acute sense of when to employ their spiritual powers and when not to, then they will find that they will not be looking at the less savory aspects of the spirit world all the time.

Should they fail to do so, they will soon find themselves abusing their psychic powers, and in the end they will become slaves of those powers rather than their masters. In that case probably the best thing for them to do would be to try to become completely average members of the material world with outstanding personality characteristics that will win the respect of their neighbors. Only when they learn how to live a good life independent on their psychic powers can they live in true accord with the divine world. What then should a psychic who has been overexposed to the ugly side of the spirit world do in practical terms?

In order to get away from this sordidness, they should immerse themselves in beautiful natural scenery, listen to exquisite music and otherwise try to experience as much of the beauty in this world as possible. The rationale here is to try to partake of the beauty of heaven itself by finding the closest possible experiences here on earth.

By doing so, the "poison" that resulted from looking at the evil spirits for too long can be counteracted. This might seem very simple to do, but the fact is that very few people in this situation actually do so. Sometimes I have actresses or fashion models come to me for advice. I take advantage of the opportunity to gaze at their beauty in order to cleanse my vision. However, I have to admit that when I look at some of these same individuals from the view of the spirit world, I feel like vomiting....so black are their souls. Other ways to refresh and purify your spirit include enjoying beautiful natural scenery and then drawing pictures of what you see or practicing calligraphy.

The Predisposing Attitude

"**A**s a result of careful research and analysis regarding the relative merits of optimism and pessimism, I have come to the conclusion that optimism is the correct approach to life. Therefore I shall henceforth adopt an optimistic attitude."

I do not think you will be able to find anyone who thinks in such a fashion. Before any such research and analysis even begins, a person will have the feeling that a certain view on life is correct for him. This inherent outlook will decide whether he decides to call himself an optimist or pessimist.

Religious faith operates in the same fashion.

"As a result of research into the divine, I have come to the conclusion that the gods really do exist." You will not find anyone going around saying something like this. Whether or not a person professes to believe in a god or gods depends on whether they really want to believe in them. It is not a cold rational decision. Rational arguments for the existence of the divine are only developed later by a person who is a believer. And whether or not another person accepts these arguments will largely depend on whether he was presupposed to do so. So some people will sincerely believe, while others will reject even the most convincing proof.

The same goes for our taste in reading. Some people only read very sad books that tell only of failure in life. Not surprisingly they frequently develop a negative attitude as a result, saying to themselves, "Just as I thought. Human existence is nothing but suffering and futility." But this attitude does not really derive from the books that they have read. It is a result of the way of thinking they had before they ever picked up those books, namely "Oh life is after all nothing but emptiness and bitterness." So they naturally choose books that will reaffirm this view of life. The reason that the contents of these books evokes a responsive mood in their hearts is that they reflect what the person already feels.

As a result, such a person gradually develops a negative mind-set that basically determines how he views life. In turn his way of viewing reality and style of thinking become his ideology. It might go under the name of nihilism or pessimism, or something else.

The philosopher Arthur Schopenhauer (1788-1860) wrote that the way an individual views reality is conditioned by the books he reads and the people he talks to. All that is absorbed becomes the basis of the principles that guide his life; so in a sense these concepts or principles derive from intuition. In other words, there is a chain reaction at work here: intuition – conceptualization – way of perceiving reality.

Intuition is nothing other than the predisposing attitude I referred to earlier. But from where does this climate of the soul ultimately derive? Well to put it simply, when it is of a positive nature it is thanks to your guardian spirits, but when it is of a negative nature it is the result of malicious mischief by various kinds of evil spirits. More specifically, this predisposition results from the spiritual waves given off by these various spirits. In other words, the spirit world is the ultimate origin of all these predispositions. And that too is where a person's "primary soul" dwells. If a man's basic disposition is normally bright and lively, we can say that while he is alive his "primary soul" is dwelling in a good spirit world. So our predisposing attitude is determined by what spirit world we are in at a given time, and there is often a constant give-and-take between good predispositions and evil predispositions.

For example, you might have a spirit that is tied to one physical place and a discontented ancestor jointly haunting a particular house where you are living. In such a case, negative thinking caused by the spiritual vibrations they give off would be impossible to avoid. You would therefore become very susceptible to negative thoughts, like "Life is useless" or "Oh, I am suffering so much."

Conversely, things operate to your benefit when you are subject to positive spiritual vibrations. Healthy predispositions are the result. Let me give you an example.

Nana Sato is a multi-talented woman: an artist, singer-songwriter, announcer, photographer and video director. How can a person be so versatile? She remembers how when she was a child her mother made her practice gymnastics with the eventual goal of getting to the Olympics. However, one day when she was practicing, she fell during a turn and hit her head hard. "I've been crazy ever since," she likes to say.

No doubt she means it as a joke.

Sato also has a habit of saying, "Wow, that's fantastic!"

Her very unusual voice causes a sense of peace and harmony in the hearts of all who hear her.

I clearly remember her story of how she got involved in photography. "I just thought taking pictures would be so cool," she recalls. However, encouragement from others caused her to start taking the whole thing seriously.

No doubt her involvement in music recording and films also began with her happy-go-lucky attitude, and was a product of her positive predisposition.

It is precisely because she likes to view everything in life as "wonderful" and as an adventure, that her inner spiritual world helps to transform the things and experiences she encounters in her daily life into wonderful opportunities. And each new wonderful experience opens up opportunities for similar experiences. Success follows on success because of this natural predisposition to see the good in life. And it is for that reason that Sato always retains a fresh, natural and positive attitude. This in turn has made possible the full flowering of the latent talents she always had inside of her.

But the fact is that she was once under the influence of evil spirits.

When I first met Sato, she was given to only dark, gloomy conversation. When I asked her why that was so, she replied as follows: "Right now I'm preoccupied with taking photos of graves. Japanese tombs tend to be scary. But there are usually flowers growing around graves in Europe and they somehow seem so splendid."

Such an activity in itself was fine. But while she was taking pictures of graves, Western wandering ghosts crowded around her in tremendous numbers. As a result, her own features came to take on the look of a ghost. So she came to see me for a spiritual purification.

Afterwards she said with glee, "Wow, my head feels so lucid. I feel just wonderful." She had completely recovered her natural high spirits. You might say that Sato was a classic case of a person in whom negative and positive spiritual vibrations were vying for supremacy.

In any event, since our predispositions to a large extent determine the course of our lives, we cannot afford to ignore that fact. Always bear this predisposition uppermost in mind.

Throughout the ages, philosophers and other thinkers have advocated a wide variety of philosophies, everything from existentialism to materialism. You might say that each of the philosophical viewpoints grew out of a mixture of the historical circumstances and the interplay of the thinker's own spirit and the spiritual vibrations received from various other spirits.

For example, if I were to give an explanation of Karl Marx's theory of capitalism from the standpoint of the spirit world, I would note the strong sense of grievance he had towards society that in turn attracted a tenacious spirit. The resulting interaction became the foundation of his wisdom. The hatred Marx bore for social injustice combined with the vengeful character of the spirit he had attracted to create the atmosphere needed for the writing of *Das Kapital*, a book filled with rage.

Nevertheless, the truth is that the situation was somewhat more complicated than this. There was involvement by a major god. Marx was not the messenger of an evil god. It would probably be more accurate to refer to him as the messenger of a demon god. Some of my Christian readers might object strenuously to this analysis, but it is true.

In any event, we are in an age when the socialist or communist camp is increasingly recognizing that coercion cannot create a better society and is therefore taking on a social-democratic hue, while the Free World nations are adopting techniques from socialism for government organization and leadership. A new type of global economy is emerging as a result. When the point is reached that the Socialist and Free World camps have established the same kind of economic structure and strategies, then the stage will be set for a world government under the auspices of the United Nations.

Overall, we can divide the global economy into three major economic blocs and one smaller one. In other words, we now have a four-sided global economy. Japan might be one of the leaders of the largest economic bloc, but things could change drastically overnight and it could then find itself as merely the head of the smallest economic block.

At that time Japan may have only the fortieth or forty-fifth largest GNP in the world, but it could be a real center of culture, the arts, religion, scholarship, education and science with its own distinctive nature as a cultural and economic leader. One thing is for sure, the world is going to change tremendously in the days to come. For one thing, Canada should have the largest GNP in the world by then. But the changes will take far longer than 30 years or so. We are talking about a time considerably down the line.

But when that day comes, Marx will probably be viewed as the messenger of a god that was out to change the very roots of human society. Still no doubt he will be viewed as a devil by people of religious persuasion for his avowed rejection of religion and the divine as evidenced by his statement, "Religion is the opium of the masses."

It should be pointed out, however, that the Supreme Creator who made heaven and earth did not create religion alone. He created politics, economics, academic learning, the arts – indeed all creative facets of human existence. Religion is nothing more than one of many factors.

So if we view politics, economics, religion, academic learning and so on as manifestations of the power of this Supreme Creator then in a broad sense Marx too may be regarded as a messenger of this divinity. So he certainly did not do bad things for the sake of doing bad things. The outcome of his actions may appear to be indistinguishable from evil. And indeed until the day when all men are happy, Marx will continue to hold the form of a reddish-black serpent, and be identified with the position of the devils.

But at that time people will realize what a vital role Marx played in human history. True, those in the free market camp might consider him a veritable devil or monster. But with the gradual improvement in the global economy that has occurred to the fine degree that we see today, although in the past Marx might have been thought of as the mailed fist of the devil as far as world history is concerned, we should realize that he indirectly helped to produce the system of prosperity and peace that we enjoy today. The day will come when people will know that Marx was really a manifestation of the will of Kunitokodachi no Mikoto, the head of the terrestrial spirit world, who all regard with awe and dread. All will know this when the proper time arrives.

Encouraging Proper Predispositions

As I explained earlier, intuition, conceptualization and our general outlook follow in a sequential flow and shape how we look at life. If you understand this point, it will be most helpful in understanding why philosophies and so on really are not very useful for judging reality.

Since everything can be traced back to the original predisposition, even if you engage in weighty research into philosophy or systems of thought, you are not likely to find a solution to your own problems. Philosophies, systems of thought or doctrines are nothing but surface manifestations. Unless you recognize the universe of preconceptions that lie behind them, you are certain to lose your way in a maze.

Ideally, the thing to do is to try to actively and tirelessly develop a healthy predisposition and then buttress it with appropriate philosophy, thought, ethics or doctrines. In that way the spiritual sense will function completely as the director of the intellect. Only in this way will the two play their proper respective roles.

What then do we need to do in order to cultivate a proper predisposition? How exactly do we go about developing bright sensibilities and appropriate dynamics for our primary soul?

The first thing to do is to live in a good physical environment.

The second thing to do is to associate with good people to the greatest extent possible. Third, get out into beautiful nature as much as possible. Fourth, try to achieve as serene a spirit as possible. Fifth, speak in a manner that will help to cultivate a bright, progressive view of human life and read virtuous books infused with the miraculous power and soul of language that will do likewise. Sixth, expose yourself to art so that you can develop your aesthetic tastes. Seventh, choose an interior decor and color coordination for your home that will foster good feelings and a healthy spirit. Eighth, choose fashions that will make you brighter in spirit and more forward-thinking. Ninth, choose a home or room that has plenty of sunlight. Tenth, learn the habit of prayer so that you may enjoy better thinking and sensibilities. Eleventh, be more careful in your attitude, speech and etiquette when dealing with people, so that you will make a favorable impression on others. If you follow these simple suggestions, I think that you will find that you will develop a better personality – brighter, more keenly motivated, more progressive, more beautiful. In other words you will become the kind of person who appreciates the many things there are to enjoy in this life of ours. You will become an individual who feels more deeply, recognizes reality more clearly and is blessed by good fortune.

It is important to live in as suitable environment as possible. But the fact is that without even intending to do so, many people end up choosing a poor environment for themselves. What can such individuals do?

The Chinese monk who founded the Rinzai school of Zen made an insightful comment in this regard, when he said, "If you center on yourself wherever you may be at, all truth will immediately reveal itself there." In other words, no matter where you may be consider yourself as the center point. And if you not only disregard the influence of your environment but instead yourself influence that environment you will discover the truth.

To put it another way, no matter what you may be doing, always seek to discover and expose your true self, not just your ego, but the essential spiritual attributes of your being. This really means that no matter how much you may be suffering or how dejected you may be, do not let relations with other people or other environmental factors influence you. Instead, you yourself should influence your environment. By thus acting on the basis of your true self, you will be able to overcome any perplexities or problems and express that true self as it should be expressed. In any event, this is the basic meaning of the Zen insight.

By adhering to this philosophy and learning to express your real intentions, you can develop a strength of will that can allow you to take a separate route from that indicated by your predispositions. You will thus become a person capable of controlling your environment and eventually you will be able to create your own appropriate environment. What this means is that no matter what your family background, who your parents were, what your nationality or ethnic origins are, or how wealthy your parents are...no matter what the extraneous circumstances that surround you, the environment you live in, you will be able to ignore all this along with all ignorance and inadequacies, and work for your own personal growth and progress. By overcoming all these environmental factors, you can become a man of wisdom and truth who understands who he really is. The spirit of that long-deceased saintly Chinese monk is spurring you on to do exactly that. He has applied such harsh but kindly pressure on me on numerous occasions.

For example, say you are working at a place where human relations are difficult. Before judging the environment in that workplace, first try to develop yourself in as positive and constructive a manner as possible, striving to help improve that human interaction. Of course, you may have to ignore those people who prove totally uncooperative, keep inevitable disagreements short, and calmly try to find satisfaction from your job whether you are coming out ahead or not in the interoffice maneuvering. Do so and I guarantee that your colleagues will take notice. It is a question of differences in the amount of moral courage displayed. If you show the necessary grit, your fellow workers will definitely take a new tack themselves, and you may see that some of them begin acting totally different. In this way you can open up bold new vistas for yourself as well.

All of this may seem to be somewhat contradictory to the earlier discussion of the need to place yourself in the proper environment, but I can ensure you it is not.

The most important thing to bear in mind in the beginning is that you should try to put yourself in as good an environment as possible. When no matter how you try that proves impossible, you may take it as a sign that heaven intends to test you. You are being told that instead of remaining a person who is influenced by his environment, you need to become the audacious kind of fellow who goes out and tries to change that environment. No passive acceptance of a bad lot for you. Remember too that an environment that may be perfect for some things would be the worst possible one for other things. Life is never that simple; it is a constant flux and interaction of numerous variables. So even when faced with what seem like the worst possible conditions, try to find a way to boldly turn the tables and achieve greater personal growth.

Or think of it this way, whether you find yourself in a good or bad environment, it really all boils down to subjectivity. For example, you find people who are living in what would be judged by any objective criteria as very fortunate circumstances. Yet they are thoroughly miserable and dissatisfied. At the same time, you also see many people in far less fortunate circumstances who are quite satisfied with their lot.

In other words, whether a particular environment is good or bad really depends on the standards of judgment of the individual involved. In the end, whether that environment is good or bad is totally dependent on the willpower and effort and ability of the individual to attain his goals. For that reason, even if by objective social standards a particular environment may be inferior, if an individual's own criteria for judging are more flexible, he may judge that environment to be tolerable. A person who never forsakes his desire to find happiness in his experiences will find relief in that very attitude. This kind of individual, who is self-directed and knows the importance of predispositions, will as a matter of course attract friendly spirits of goodness to his side. And more often than not such people will be blessed with incredible good fortune.

CHAPTER 3

Spiritual Purification
Can Change Your Luck
in a Flash

Why is Spiritual Purification Necessary?

Up till this point in the book I have addressed several important questions, including: "What are spirits?" "In what form does the influence of these spirits affect human beings?" "Which kinds of people are especially susceptible to the influence of the spirits?" "What kinds of places are dangerous?" "What kind of posture should we adopt in regards to the spirits?" So I think you already understand the gist of how these things work.

But I would like to emphasize that the things I am discussing in this book are not meant to encourage you to become recklessly interested in the ways of the spirits. Rather I hope that you will seek to increase your correct, necessary knowledge in this respect, so as to be able to acquire through this knowledge the proper type of spiritual faith. In that way during your everyday life you can constantly strive for progress, development and harmony by seeking to deal conscientiously and wholeheartedly with whatever immediate task you may face.

If you can manage to live in such a manner, then you will find that your sense of commitment and approach to life will greatly impress your guardian spirits while driving away any malevolent spirits that may be hovering around. People who live in such a manner are achieving a spiritual purification without their even realizing it, and in turn this allows them to continue to progress, develop and advance to a higher spiritual plateau and become the kind of human beings that the gods want them to be.

When you think about it, this state of affairs seems the most natural thing possible, and you might be wondering what on earth is new about all this I am writing about.

I would be the first to concede that point. The things I am saying are the most commonplace, natural things around.

But the point is that the truths that men should embrace are to be found precisely among the commonplace and obvious. I will not deny that many people think that the essential truths of life are to be found concealed somewhere in difficult to comprehend philosophical and religious tomes. But they could not be more wrong. The truths of eternal life are hidden just beneath the surface in every humdrum instant of our daily lives. And it is the people who are able to discover them and make them part of their own reality who deserve to be considered as true masters of the art of living.

But the sad thing is that very few of these masters appear in the world. Most people become preoccupied trying to discover the essential truths in difficult books, and instead become trapped in a morass of doubt and uncertainty, while their souls wallow in a world of confusion. And because of their style of accumulating spiritual knowledge, which simply confirms their existing beliefs, the mirrors of their souls with time become more and more clouded, and they create chinks in their armor through which evil spirits can enter and take possession of them. This is the harsh reality.

Nevertheless, these people who insist on continuing their quest for spiritual truth are the lucky ones. Most people do not feel it makes a difference what form truth, love or sincerity take. They feel it is sufficient to enjoy the present moment to the fullest. I am convinced the vast majority of people are really like this. But for that very reason, because they do not have any central support within their will, they fall easy prey to the various spiritual pitfalls laid for them by evil spirits.

In this regard, I would point out that within one of the purification prayers of the Shinto religion there is the expression "Build thick the support pillars of the grand shrine on firm bedrock..." I hasten to note that this expression has a deeper significance than what it seems to be saying at first sight.

The deeper meaning is this: "If we are firm of spirit and determined, and thus establish a solid pillar of spiritual willpower and faith, then this more than anything else will induce the gods to consider us as holy 'shrine pillars,' and each one of us can become a sacred dwelling place or shrine in this world for the gods to descend into." In other words, there will be no room for wicked spirits to pry into and we will become righteous tabernacles for the gods and benevolent spirits.

But when people live the kind of inappropriate life that I described earlier for too long their ways of thinking and living become hidebound and they find it next to impossible to reverse this self-destructive pattern through the force of their own will. Their feeble efforts simply cannot create the proper attitude required to work all out for progress, spiritual growth and development and to give that last ounce of effort it takes to make a spiritual breakthrough to a higher level.

Why should that be so? Well, over the years the evil spirits have built nice little nests for themselves in the environment of spiritual inertia that these people have self-engendered. They have entrapped the souls of these unfortunates in layer upon layer of wickedness.

I conduct spiritual purifications for such individuals. These spiritual purifications are designed to cut through the deep mists of negative thinking that the evil spirits have shrouded the souls of these people in.

And if the people who undergo these spiritual purifications are willing to make the minimum required effort, they can transform their way of thinking into a healthy, positive form. People who have been obsessed with the negative can through a bit of cooperation start looking at things in a positive fashion.

And once a person starts thinking about things in a positive way, then he or she can develop and maintain positive personality characteristics and a natural result will be that all varieties of evil spirits do not dare to approach close.

In my book *Your Place in the Divine Order* I noted that the inherent karma or spiritual legacy of every family differs and the fortunes of individuals are affected by this heritage. That being so, it only makes sense that even people who undergo spiritual purifications that drive out evil spirits do not necessarily become completely cured of existing illnesses. Nor is there any guarantee that their personalities will change completely and their lives will change for the better. Nevertheless, there are quite a few cases in which miraculous recoveries and changes occur that leave doctors, friends and family members astounded.

In this third section of the book then, I would like to discuss some of the particulars of spiritual purifications. The actual details of the methods, types of spirit interference encountered, and so on, as well as an in-depth description of the reality of the spiritual world are contained in my earlier book *Divine Powers*. Those of you interested in those aspects of the problem, kindly consult that book. Here I would like to discuss a specific case and look at the situation from a different angle.

What I did was record a verbatim discussion among myself, Kazuko Yamamoto (pseudonym), a woman who I conducted a spiritual purification for, and a friend of mine named Takayama, who is interested in spiritual matters. I will be very pleased if it proves useful to your understanding of the process and significance of spiritual purification.

The Miracle of Spiritual Purification

Fukami: Recently your friend underwent spiritual purification. How did things turn out afterwards?

Yamamoto: She safely gave birth to a healthy baby and has already been released from the hospital.

Fukami: She's already had her baby? That's fine. The placenta was considered abnormal, I understand.

Yamamoto: That's true. The doctors had said that it would be absolutely impossible for her to bear the child. They termed it a miracle.

Fukami: She went through a "photo spiritual purification," didn't she?

Yamamoto: That's correct. And then a week later an ultrasonic scan showed that the placenta had become normal.

Takayama: By "later" I assume you mean after the spiritual purification?

Yamamoto: Yes. Actually, she had already gone through one ceremony earlier, but it did not seem to have much effect. Your disciple Yasuto Nishitani, who himself performed the spiritual purification, remarked at that time that we seemed to be dealing with an especially stubborn evil spirit, so that it had not been completely driven out as of yet. So we tried again with the photograph. Then the tests a week after that showed that the fetus was perfectly normal.... The doctors said that there was no scientific foundation for such a change, so they couldn't believe it.

Takayama: What exactly does a 'photo spiritual purification' involve? To be honest, I have no idea what you're talking about here...

Fukami: This method is used when for some reason the principal cannot be present. While looking at the photo of the person, the master of spiritual purification imagines that the person is actually present. In other words, the soul of that person is summoned out of the body of the person and comes flying to the master of spiritual purification, while his flies to her, thereby making possible the purification. It is a case of "remote-control spiritual purification."

Takayama: What kind of spirits were Ms. Yamamoto's friend possessed by?

Fukami: Well, first of all I should make it clear that her photo was not possessed at all. The reason that we used it is that if you look at a person's photo, you can more or less tell what his or her karma is. You can also deal with the spirits that are possessing the person, telling them to come or go as you please through the spiritual purification rite.

Yamamoto: In the case of my friend, she was possessed by a spirit of lust....

Fukami: A spirit of lust or passion. That's usually the case when a woman is suffering some physical problem with her reproductive system. It is the manifestation of a woman's spirit of rancor or revenge. Tuberculosis is also usually caused by a malicious female spirit. However, another disease that affects the chest area, asthma, is most often a signal from the person's ancestors that she needs to mend her ways.

Takayama: Really? A warning from his ancestors?

Curse of a Tree Spirit

Fukami: There are also cases in which a woman's illness is caused by a curse by a tree spirit.

Takayama: A curse by a tree spirit?

Fukami: Yes, these are the spirits of trees that have been cut down. Especially in the case of cherry, camellia, persimmon, apple or other trees that bear flowers or fruit, if the tree is cut down then the spirit inside is likely to put a curse on a woman and inflict her with a woman's disease or some ailment of the hips or knees. It's really weird, but when cryptomerias, pines, poplars, beeches or evergreen oaks are felled, it tends to be a man who becomes a target of revenge for the angry spirit.

Takayama: What happens if a woman cuts down a cryptomeria or pine?

Fukami: The spirit still goes looking for a man. In many cases her eldest son. In families where the husband always seems to die of an apoplectic stroke, you often find that his ancestors cut down a tree. When there is a persistent tree spirit like that it often came from a large pine or cryptomeria that had been felled at some time in the past. Besides apoplectic strokes, they also cause cerebral hemorrhages. But strokes are most common.

Takayama: What about when women are cursed?

Fukami: As I mentioned earlier, if the tree cut is of a flower- or fruit-bearing variety, then in many cases the woman who has been cursed will develop some kind of female disease. In cases of a uterine blockage or whatever, the cause is frequently either the curse of a wraith or dead spirit of a vengeful woman, or else a tree spirit. You have to look to one or other of these two causes. Of course, there are also many cases in which the trouble is being caused by possession by an ancestor spirit which has been condemned to the hell of passions.

Takayama: Anything else interesting to add about the tree spirits?

Fukami: Now that you mention it, I can recall a very interesting case. A fellow came to me for a spiritual purification whose family had for generations been woodcutters. He was afflicted by a condition known as *shokei* or cheirospasm. In other words, he found himself with severe writer's cramp and was unable to put words on paper. Since he came from a long line of woodcutters, I theorized that a wood spirit might have something to do with it. But when I conducted the spiritual purification, I found out that I had been completely wrong. It had nothing to do with a curse by a tree spirit.

Takayama: But his ancestors had been woodcutters, hadn't they?

Fukami: That's true. But the tree spirits hadn't sought revenge against the woodcutters.

Takayama: Where did they go to then?

Fukami: As a matter of fact, they took possession of the owner of the forests where these woodcutters had worked. The owner who had actually ordered the trees to be felled was the one who was cursed. Since woodcutters only follow orders when they chop down the trees, they aren't necessarily cursed.

Takayama: That makes sense. But what then was the cause for the man's palsy of the hand?

Fukami: Well, it seems he had an ancestor who had no hands. That ancestor had been condemned to hell and he had taken possession of his descendent in order to try to win release from the netherworld. The man who was possessed by that evil spirit came to share some of the suffering of his ancestor. The man had been trapped in this symbiotic relationship with his ancestor since his youth and he was the only one of his relatives who was so afflicted.

Upper Body Trouble Indicates a Warning by an Ancestor

Takayama: That sounds like a similar situation to that of Yamamoto's friend....

Fukami: That's right. There we're dealing with a lustful spirit. The spirit of an ancestor, who had been condemned to hell because of some problem connected with lust, united with a vengeful wraith to take possession of her. But this is something of a special case. As I mentioned earlier, in the case of possession by a female spirit bent on revenge, the victim in most cases suffers from a woman's problem or tuberculosis. However, with other diseases of the chest, for example asthma, usually the manifestation should be viewed as a warning from an ancestor.

Yamamoto: You mean an ancestor might cause a disease as a way of giving warning?

Fukami: There are cases like that. Ancestors cause such problems if they're trying to get a certain message across. For example: Stop fooling around so much and start acting right. Make offerings to your ancestors like you're supposed to. Get out and take proper care of the family graves. Help me get out of hell. There are several possible reasons for them taking this approach and afflicting their descendants with some sickness. In many cases, as I mentioned earlier, the admonition takes the form of asthma. In other cases, it might be ozena, hardness of hearing or something else.

Yamamoto: A warning or a grudge – how do you make the distinction?

Fukami: Usually an illness that affects the part of the body above the neck indicates a warning from an ancestor. On the other hand, if the ailment is found in a part of the body below the neck, it was probably caused by an ancestor who is now in hell. Well anyhow that's the way things usually work.

Takayama: What about with the woman we were talking about? Did she get better after the spiritual purification?

Yamamoto: Yes, she got completely well. And she had a fine baby even though people said she never could.

Fukami: Well, I was really worried. I wondered how things had turned out.

Manipulation From Behind the Scenes

Yamamoto: Now, she got completely well. Although it seems that she was a bit shocked at first when she was told that her suffering was due to a lustful spirit....I had my doubts too. Since she and I have many things in common, I started wondering whether I too am not now at the mercy of a ghost consumed by sexual passion. When I mentioned my fears to her, she said that I must come to see you...

Fukami: So that's how it happened.

Yamamoto: Yes. And when I talked with you, you said that this really seemed to be the explanation for my condition. You told me that one of my ancestors was a man who had made a lot of women cry. And one or more of these women were taking out their vengeful feelings towards him on me. And you also explained that the reason that I always had difficulty with my interpersonal relationships was the curse placed on me by those vengeful women.

Fukami: That's exactly how it is.

Yamamoto: Even when it looks like things might go well in my life, they just don't work out. I myself don't know why it should be, but I'm always attracted to people with whom I cannot form healthy relationships. And I'm not attracted to people with whom things might work out well.

Fukami: By the way, what was your mother's maiden name?

Yamamoto: Kato.

Fukami: I can see that one of your ancestors on your mother's side was a navy man. I think he was probably with one of the naval units that cooperated with the 16th Century warlord Oda Nobunaga, who united the core area of Japan.

Yamamoto: An ancestor on my mother's side?

Fukami: Yes, that's correct. I can see that he drove many of his enemies into the water where they drowned. My spiritual intuition shows me a picture of 319 men. The overwhelming feelings of vengeance of these 319 individuals has consolidated into a single spirit that has manifested itself in the form of a gigantic snake some 20 meters in length. The curse we are dealing with from this serpent comes from the spirits of men who died by suicide combined with those of your ancestors who have been condemned to hell.

Yamamoto: Then there really isn't any lustful spirit involved?

Fukami: No, it's not that simple. Unfortunately a lustful spirit is also involved. But there is another spirit behind that lustful spirit that is manipulating it. It is that huge snake that was formed through the merger of the spirits of hundreds of men.

Yamamoto: Are all of those men ancestors in the Kato family?

Fukami: No, not at all. They were men who were murdered by your ancestors – 319 of them. Because your ancestors killed them, they are directing their curse of revenge against you, the descendent. This 20-meter-long snake into which they have all incorporated their vengeful spirits has horns growing from its head and the faces of all these men are visible on its scales. The entire body of this enormous serpent consists of nothing but faces, faces and more faces.

Yamamoto: And it is because of this curse that I simply cannot find happiness.

Fukami: That's right. It's because the desire for revenge among them is so strong. Usually when men are killed, their spirits become tied to the scenes of their death, for example such spirits still haunt old battlefields. But when the deaths come about because of betrayal, deception or some other such reason, the spirits of the murdered men scream out at those who have committed the injustice, "You bastards! We will have our revenge." And thus their desire for vengeance continues strong through the generations.

Normally, these vengeful spirits wait for the most opportune moment to exact their revenge. It would not be so sweet if they attacked their intended victim when he or she is in their teens or twenties. Far better to wait until the person is ready to reach the height of his or her career – on the eve of achieving the ambition to become Prime Minister or company president, for example.

Then cancer strikes. Or heart trouble. And the victim thinks, "What after all is this life I've worked so hard over 40 years to build?" Then he or she sinks into the depths of despair. The vengeful spirit is then overjoyed. How sweet is revenge when it is not premature, but instead comes when the object of the vendetta is about to grasp the brass ring. These evil, vengeful spirits are quite clever, you know.

Yamamoto: My case is exactly like what you describe.

Fukami: I bet it is. And just remember, there are 319 spirits involved here. And all of them are samurai, bright fellows who normally will not exact vengeance themselves. They prefer to get a lustful spirit to do their dirty work for them.

Takayama: For that reason it is easy for clairvoyants who rely on direct communication with the spirits to make an error and believe that there is simply a lustful spirit at work here.

Fukami: That's correct. Spiritualists who rely on a perfunctory glimpse into the world of the spirits end up being completely fooled. To merely *look* or *listen* is not enough. *Look*, but doubt; *listen*, but doubt. Always question your initial conclusions. And only after employing intuitive powers that are firmly grounded in correct spiritual knowledge can you make a conclusive judgment that your first assessment was correct after all. For that reason, even clairvoyants – no I should say, especially clairvoyants – need to develop highly attuned spiritual sensibilities backed up by true knowledge and training.

Takayama: That certainly makes sense. But to get back to the case of vengeful spirits who lay curses on the families of those who did them wrong, how long do these curses remain in effect?

Fukami: Usually they last for six or seven generations. If the main branch of the victimized family dies out, the family name is changed or there is no heir, then the vengeful spirits as a rule call it quits. But in such cases, the vengeful spirit still retains the grudge, and therefore cannot enter into the peace of the spirit world but remains in a kind of limbo.

Takayama: How then can they return to the spirit world?

Spiritual Purification of Vengeful Spirits

Fukami: Vengeful spirits who lay curses on the living are seeking revenge precisely because they themselves are suffering. Their grudge in turn prevents them from returning to the spirit world. So this feeling has to be dispelled for them to obtain release.

Takayama: Exactly how is that done?

Fukami: I jokingly refer to it as "the pro wrestler's secret method for counterattacking." In other words, you achieve victory to a certain extent by offering oneself as a substitute. Thus, you can get rid of the grudge. Let me explain. Watch a pro wrestling match and you will see that often at the start the bad guy seems to be having everything his own way and is wiping up the mat with the hero. But then at the very end, the good guy turns the tables and wins out over his unprincipled opponent. That's what often happens in matches involving the famous Antonio Inoki. Just when you think Inoki is done for, he will flip his opponent over and pin him to the mat. That's the kind of thing I'm talking about.

Takayama: I guess that's why your face often loses all its color and you fall into a swoon before performing a spiritual purification.

Fukami: That's true. If I don't act like I'm a bit in trouble at the beginning, the vengeful spirit is not likely to be satisfied. And while I'm on the ropes so to speak, I make a very careful spiritual assessment of the situation and then wait for the appropriate moment to react and counterattack.

Takayama: I see. I understand now exactly what happens.

Fukami: Of course, it is only by experiencing a certain amount of pain that one can develop the spirit of compassion needed to accomplish the mission. But then when you really want to, you can handle spiritual purifications with as much ease as Mike Tyson handles opponents in the ring. But the point is, you are in the position to help the person being exorcised clearly realize that a spirit is seeking revenge because of the actions of his or her ancestors. You want that person to realize the horribleness of the vengeful spirit that is causing his or her own suffering, the seriousness of the crimes of the ancestors at fault, and the deep karmic ties that unite the descendants with those ancestors and those whom they harmed. For that reason I find it advisable to allow the fullest mount of suffering possible to be experienced during the spiritual purification.

Takayama: That seems....It's an extremely difficult approach to take....Especially when you are in the position to counterattack at the time of your choosing.

Fukami: If the person being exorcised has a cold or otherwise is not in tip-top shape, it's best to get it over as soon as possible. But if you always do so, then the spiritual purification becomes a work without devotion and the effort will to a large extent be a waste.

Takayama: You seem to really enjoy the effort.

Fukami: Penetrating disguises, escaping traps laid in your path, bearing the pain until you are ready to counterattack...well, I guess you might compare my pleasures to those of a pro wrestler.

Takayama: That's amazing....

Fukami: However, even though I speak of "counterattack," it is really not an exercise of power at all. You must act with total love and sincerity. Since the spiritual world is a world of incorporeal wishes and thoughts, no matter how hard we struggle, we still cannot win in physical terms against the spirit of a dead person. When you get right down to it, in such a case your opponent is somebody who has been dead for many, many years.

Takayama: A long deceased person....

Fukami: On the other hand, we are part flesh and part spirit. And we are naturally not as familiar with the spirit world as are the deceased. So no matter how hard we might try, can we really expect to conquer in a match of wits?

I like to tell would-be clairvoyants or psychics to try dying on the spot. After all anyone who is dead is clairvoyant. If they do so, what they will discover is that the spirits can tell in an instant what kind of frame of mind you are in when you are conducting a spiritual purification – whether you are acting with true love and sincerity, or whether you are merely trying to entrap and drive them away. If an ascetic or like individual performs an exorcism through force of will power or psychokinesis, any *tengu*, dragon or *Inari* fox which seeks to possess him during the process is liable to cause the vengeful spirit being exorcised to flee in panic. So terrifying are they.

Takayama: Fear grips its heart.

Fukami: Yes, it becomes paralyzed with fear. But even in cases like this where the spirit that has placed the curse concludes that the person conducting the spiritual purification is the more powerful and takes to its heels, it is certain to return right afterwards because it has not undergone any change of heart. It will stay away for good only if it has undergone a real change of heart. Otherwise it will keep coming back no matter how many times you repeat the spiritual purification. Furthermore, its grudge will be even stronger when it does return...

Takayama: So love and sincerity are absolutely essential.

Fukami: That's correct. More than anything else the person who performs the spiritual purification has to fill his soul with these two feelings. However, that does not mean that just because a person possesses love and sincerity, he or she is ready to perform spiritual purifications. Far from it. In order to be able to completely eliminate the grudge, you must also be familiar with the required techniques.

Takayama: What kind of techniques are you referring to?

Fukami: Before I get into that I would first like to talk about something else. Do you believe that men can be induced to reform or undergo a change of heart simply on the basis of being preached to?

For example, if you tell someone, "You are mistaken in this regard and should change your ways," what do you think the likelihood is that he or she will take your advice? A superior individual might do so right away, but that approach won't work with the average person. Even if a person accepts the advisability of the suggestion in the mind, he will reject it at the gut level. In fact, the more average a person is the more likely that is to occur.

It's naturally even more difficult to get a spirit who has been consumed with a desire for revenge for a long period to have a change of heart. Even if you warn, "Give up your desire for vengeance and return to the spirit world or you will continue to suffer in hell for all eternity," such a spirit is likely to reply, "I'm aware of that fact, but do you think I can forgive after having suffered so much? Even should I be consigned to an endless hell, it doesn't matter the least to me. I will not forgive that person's family no matter what."

Takayama: Therefore, persuasion apparently doesn't have much effect. So what can you do?

Fukami: As I explained in *Divine Powers*, in order to achieve a true change of heart in such a spirit you have to explain the karmic ties that bind it to a previous lifetime. People do not suffer or undergo bitter experiences unless there is an underlying karmic cause. Especially in cases where people are killed or feel forced to commit suicide, you can be sure that the laws of karma are at work in the form of ties to a previous life.

Takayama: Karmic connections with a previous life?

Fukami: Yes, karmic connections with a previous life. For example, let's take the case of Ms. Yamamoto here. If you consider how she has led such a sincere, straightforward life, you must ask yourself why she should have to suffer so. At first, she didn't have a clue. It was only after she found out that there were 319 men betrayed by her ancestor in a past age who had come to torment her that she could understand that a karmic connection was the true reason for her suffering.

Takayama: I see. So that's the way it is.

Fukami: However, even such an understanding of the situation on her part is insufficient. The reason why is that intellectual understanding is not the same as contrition. She understood that her ancestor had committed a despicable deed. But she continued to be resentful that she should have to make amends for what this ancestor did. I think that's exactly how she felt.

Yamamoto: Well, that's understandable. Anyhow, how can such a desired conversion be accomplished?

Fukami: As I explained before, the only thing you can do is explain very clearly about the ties that bind a person to a previous life – the karmic connection. There is always a reason why a person is born into a family who had an evil ancestor. You might say that such a person was destined to be born into just such a family. It is because of the deeds the person himself committed in a past life, the seeds he himself sowed, that there is this connection to past generations. If you explain that to the suffering individual then he is likely to say, "Ah, now I can see at last." And then the process of contrition can take place.

Takayama: And you have to adopt the same stance in regards to the vengeful spirits?

Fukami: Exactly.

Yamamoto: What were the previous existences of those 319 spirits who bore a grudge against various generations of my family like?

Fukami: We're talking about the Nambokucho civil war period back in the 14th century, when the northern and southern imperial courts were struggling for supremacy. They were part of the naval forces fighting for the Northern Court. They did something as nasty as your ancestor did to them, I mean. It involves poisoning. It seems like they invited their foes to a reconciliation banquet, but poisoned their food. Then when these deceived people were writhing in agony, they launched a night attack and mowed them down.

Takayama: In other words the karmic chickens have come home to roost?

Fukami: Yes, that's right.

Takayama: Do you explain these things about the workings of karma to the spirits directly?

Fukami: Yes, I explain. If you use the proper spiritual powers and powerful ritual language in explaining previous existences, then these spirits understand all. The instant after you do these things, they can see the entire picture clearly. When their numbers are great, however, just repeating the special phrases is not enough. You must actually be transported in mind to the scene of the action.

Takayama: Transported in time?

Fukami: Yes, you have to be able to visualize what happened centuries before. In the case of Ms. Yamamoto, we could actually see the mass poisoning done by the men in their previous life and the subsequent night attack and slaughter. We could see it very clearly. The faces were as clear as if we were looking at our own faces in the mirror. So these spirits each said in his soul, "Ah, it was truly like that. Now I can understand how all this came about." And because of that he could undergo the necessary penance in his soul.

Takayama: Is it really possible to show things like that to a person?

Fukami: I assure you that it is. I still have not divulged the method, but.... This is a power that is directly bestowed by the gods. Only spiritual practitioners who have been given this special power by the gods can perform this feat. So even if you knew the method for making these direct viewings of earlier happenings possible, if the gods had not willed it, you would achieve absolutely no results. But if you do have the power and you are sincere and give your utmost when sharing knowledge of these karmic connections with previous lifetimes, then even the most perverse vengeful spirit will repent.

In any event, you can be sure that people are not unhappy unless there is a reason for their unhappiness. Nor do they have accidents without cause. Nor do they suffer from bad luck. On the other hand, be aware that so-called lucky people are those who tried to make others happy in their past lives, tried to bring joy into the lives of their neighbors, tried to accumulate merit. And they no doubt are doing virtuous things in this life as well.

The basic karmic principle that good begets good and evil begets evil is eternal and unchangeable. Only when an individual can come to accept this principle with his or her whole heart, can he or she experience enlightenment and repentance. If such a change of heart does not take place, however, then even if the vengeful spirits are driven away, they are sure to return later.

Takayama: It's as you say.

Fukami: But let me hasten to add that in this case mere repentance on the part of the afflicted person is not enough.

Takayama: Huh? Even that was not enough?

Fukami: That's right. It was still inadequate. The thing is: no matter how enlightened the spirits involved become the agony they suffered as they died still remains.

They ended up saying to themselves, "I know I've done wrong, but I cannot endure this suffering and pain. What is the cause of such suffering? Ah yes, I was murdered by an ancestor of the Yamamoto family. The bastard." And with such memories still alive, once again their desire for revenge wells up anew.

Takayama: Well then, what can you do about that memory?

Fukami: If one of them has a wound, you can treat it. If they have a craving for a certain food, you can get hold of it and offer it to them. If they tear their clothing, you can change it for a new garment. If it is curry rice that someone hungers for, it can be fixed in an instant. If a spirit's "body" is covered with wounds and he is suffering terribly, he can be provided with a new incorporeal body that relieves the suffering. That is the way things operate with these spirits. Provide one with a spiritual body and he suddenly says to himself, "I feel fine now. I suffered all kinds of things, but everything is all right now. So, good-bye, everyone." Then they head back to the spirit world for good. The feelings of pleasure and relief are provided directly from the divine and spirit worlds through a special form of supernatural power. By drawing on it, you can lift the incredible suffering of the death agony from the vengeful spirits, provide them with sustenance, a change of clothing, and if a female spirit is involved, lipstick, cosmetics or whatever. And in the cases in which I have been involved, these spirits have inevitably then sped back to the spirit world.

Takayama: You do these things and then they go back to the spirit world?

Fukami: Yes, they do. But the thing is: even though we call it the spirit world, in many cases these spirits have not been there yet. I'm not joking at all. You say to them, "Now you can return to the spirit world." And they answer, "Spirit world? What on earth is that?" They are often at a total loss as to what they should do and where they should go next.

These spirits that have been existing solely for the sake of revenge have been totally preoccupied with the material world to which they have been clinging, so that they have never even realized that there is such a thing as a spiritual world. So you must gently inform them that the spirit world is much like that of the living. It has its own mountains, rivers, homes and occupations. When they finally depart for that world, the spiritual purification can be brought to an end.

Yamamoto: Spiritual purification is really no laughing matter.

Significance of Tamagushi Sprigs

Fukami: You put it very well. By the way, I forgot to add something. Who do you think it is who provides the food and clothing for these vengeful spirits?

Yamamoto: What exactly do you mean by "Who provides them?"

Fukami: I mean: who provides the money to pay for them? You have to bear in mind, the same principles that operate in our material world also operate in the spirit world. In other words, nobody gets something for nothing. These vengeful spirits don't have any money of their own. So somebody has to provide it. Do you have any idea who it is?

Yamamoto: Well, would it be the gods?

Fukami: What do you think, Mr. Takayama?

Takayama: Who could it be....I too can only think of the gods.

Fukami: No, you're wrong. The gods don't do the giving in this case. The provider of these things is the very person who is undergoing the spiritual purification.

Yamamoto: Oh, it must have been the *tamagushi* offering....

Fukami: That's right. The *tamagushi* is a sprig from the sacred *Cleyera orchnacca* tree that is offered to the gods together with a monetary offering. Strictly speaking the spirit of reverence with which the *tamagushi* offering is made to the gods becomes a form of merit in the spirit world. In turn, this expression of sincerity is transformed into clothes, food, housing or other "material" things in the spirit world. Of course, these offerings have to be transmitted via the spiritual power of the spiritualist who is acting as a medium. But whether you offer money, either a large sum or small, is totally irrelevant in itself. The important thing is that an offering is made without fail. And in all cases, the offering must be made in the proper *tamagushi* form or you will get absolutely no results. Just don't think that you can get a spiritual purification for free. Do so and you won't really be able to release that troubled spirit at all.

Yamamoto: But how much should be given in the monetary offering that accompanies this ceremony?

Fukami: The person involved should do their utmost to express his or her sincerity and seriousness. The amount of money should be enough so that it hurts the pocketbook a bit. But please don't be mistaken in this regard. I can assure you I am not out to make money from spiritual purifications. I charge for my services strictly in accordance with the rules of the spirit world. I explained all of this clearly in *Divine Powers*, but let me reiterate this point here. Let's look at the case of a Good Samaritan who gives all his earthly riches to help others. At that very instant, the individual's karma will become brand new, cleansed by his sincere action. Even should a spiritual purification be performed on such an individual, no vengeful spirit or dissatisfied ancestor will make an appearance. The reason is that an incomparable form of earthly merit is thereby created which envelops the person in a spiritual glow, so that the gods, Buddhas and most highly spiritually evolved ancestral spirits flock to protect him. As a result, evil spirits cannot approach at all, or they are deflected towards a relative, or you benefit from a form of what might be called natural spiritual purification. And as a result of this situation, the gods, Buddhas and highly placed ancestral spirits render relief to the evil spirits.

Takayama: Ah, so that's the true meaning of the *tamagushi* offering.

Fukami: But bear in mind that it is not merely a question of how much money is involved here. This money is merely a physical manifestation of the sincerity and seriousness in the heart of the person making the offering. But this physical manifestation in itself means nothing. Sincerity, or *makoto*, is expressed in speech and action as well as what is felt in the heart. Sincerity found only in the heart is not real. Sincerity expressed from the beginning in the entire person, his speech, action and thinking, is the only true form of sincerity. This true form of sincerity gratifies the gods and causes them to forgive sins. So it is not a question of the more the better, and neither is it a question of only a little bit is good enough because the heart is sincere. How big an offering is appropriate then? If you pose that question to the gods, you won't get an answer in clear percentage terms based on your annual family income. Although in Christianity that's what the ideal for believers is. Nor can I simply go and inquire, "What was your family income last year?" I myself use a certain standard for such offerings. But even if considered as a standard, it should be nothing more than a guideline that we don't try to strictly impose on others. I simply say, "I feel this much would be appropriate as a *tamagushi* offering." It's an individual decision. People with the wherewithal might feel they would like to give a substantial amount. On the other hand, those who find themselves financially strapped, students and so on, after taking an objective look at their situation, might feel that they can only make a relatively small offering. The situation varies.

Takayama: But that really seems the appropriate way to handle things. I'm sure that's so for those undergoing spiritual purifications. I guess you could call it an instance of voluntary action. Still, a lot of people are sure to be perplexed as to how much they should really give. In many cases they must also feel somewhat crass, dwelling on this particular monetary problem. So I would think that guidelines are actually best after all. They would offer people a degree of peace of mind.

Fukami: Basically, I would have to agree with you on that score....But at the same time I am not in the position to come right out and tell people what to do. Personally, I don't receive one yen of the money. The thing is, if you really want to reduce the threat to the person and bring release to the spirits, you have to make clear what needs to be done. You don't want to come right out with it. Still, you're always aware of how good it would feel just to perform the spiritual purifications for free. In the past I personally have provided services free of charge in order to accumulate merit and try to express a spirit of benevolence. And nothing could be finer than to be engaged in the business of releasing spirits, and in awakening people to the way of the gods to constantly perform works of charity for the sake of the rest of humankind. But things are not always so easy. It would be like going to a dentist who doesn't charge a fee for filling a cavity. The patient would simply say, "Thanks doc" and then be on his or her merry way. Such a patient could with this short phrase relieve himself of all future responsibility. Things would really be too easy. It's exactly the same situation when it comes to spiritual purifications. I eventually concluded that were I to conduct spiritual purifications for nothing, they clearly would be for my own benefit alone. In other words, they would make me feel self-satisfied with my benevolence and public spiritedness. But the question was whether such an approach really took into account the feelings of the vengeful spirits and the feelings of the gods, and whether the necessary change of heart was actually taking place in the heart of the individual undergoing the spiritual purification.

I concluded that such benevolence really amounted to little. On the other hand, when a person undergoing a spiritual purification accepts the reality of the situation and makes a humble offering to the gods, that money shines with unexcelled purity.

In fact, only that kind of money and the spirit in the heart of the petitioner that it reflects have the power to help him and his ancestral spirits escape their karmic plight. Only such money could be transformed into the things that would appease the vengeful spirits. A half-hearted approach won't do in this regard. And since I am performing the ceremony for an offering, I do not have the least bit of a lackadaisical attitude. Rather I pray to the gods with the greatest of seriousness, and my heart is filled with the utmost love and sincerity. In addition, the money that has been donated should be used in its entirety for the sake of pleasing the gods or contributing to society. Since in this way the money will circulate in such a manner as to achieve the greatest possible good and encourage further wisdom in spiritual affairs. Also, in such a way I have been able to reveal my powers of spiritual purification and beneficial results that follow from spiritual purifications in a way many times more effective than previously. All of this has been possible because of the custom of giving *tamagushi*. And my powers of spiritual purification and the great benefits that can result from spiritual purification have achieved much more attention than they would have otherwise. But I would be less than frank if I didn't admit that there have been complications. It may be a rather uncouth way of putting it, but I consider it a bargain if for ¥50,000 or even ¥300,000 a vengeful spirit that has been plaguing a family because of what an ancestor did long ago can be gotten rid of for good and the family fortunes thus improved. Remember it costs at least a million yen or two to buy a car. And if you want to buy some property and build a home, you're talking about spending hundreds of millions of yen. Even a burial plot and the gravestone now cost millions or tens of millions of yen. Take these things into consideration and a spiritual purification is dirt cheap.

Takayama: They certainly are a bargain.

Fukami: Be that as it may, in this particular sphere of standards of value, people tend to compare this ceremony with things like fortune-telling. That's really an insult to spirit mediums who have the proper knowledge, or the gods themselves for that matter. However, here I'm naturally talking about true spirit release. There are any number of false spiritualists and religious groups willing to take money from gullible people. But turning to such people makes almost no sense. All the person in trouble is getting is some weak propping up for his morale.

A person in trouble would do a lot better to search out on his own through careful spiritual investigation a true medium or master of spiritual purification. And if the psychic he finally decides upon seems all right, or even if the person feels a certain religious group is right for him after all, then he should ask for help and then pray with his entire being.

Generational Karma and Entry in the Family Register

Yamamoto: By the way, in speaking about revenge, does the strength of the force involved vary by the number of people or spirits who are after a person?

Fukami: Yes, it does. The greater the number involved, the greater the power of the malice.

Yamamoto: In my case then, with 319 angry spirits out to torment me, it was rather....

Fukami: Let me tell you, it was awful. On top of that, all of them were *samurai*, which meant that their manner of acting was different from that of the average person. It was like the lineup in a baseball all-star game. They were all sluggers. That's what you were facing. I can assure you it was not an ordinary situation.

Yamamoto: It's not me alone, my parents and my relatives too have all been so unhappy.

Fukami: I should think so. The entire Kato family got caught up in this business.

Yamamoto: My mother was born a Kato, but she married into the Yamamoto family. Does that mean that as a matter of course she also became subject to the unfortunate karma of the Yamamotos?

Fukami: That's right. As long as she bore the name Yamamoto, she was susceptible to that influence. In such cases, women often are very happy before they marry, but immediately afterwards start feeling unhappy or become ill. Usually, the change comes about the instant they sign their name to their husband's family register. But in your case the opposite was also involved. After the marriage your father had to bear a greater portion of the unfortunate dual family legacy.

Yamamoto: What happens if a wife's name is removed from the family register of such an ill-fated family?

Fukami: The clouds clear away immediately. If such a person's name is removed from her husband's family register, then her illness will often clear up right away. However, if she has had a child by her former husband, then the situation is different since the blood ties have been passed on. Even though the mother's name has been removed from the family register, the problem still remains. The karmic relationship is determined by the blood ties. Normally, however, once she divorces and has her name removed from the family register and takes on another family name, she will never be bothered by the bad karma again. As long as she has not had any children by her former husband, the spirits will not pursue her.

Yamamoto: In other words, when a woman marries she takes on the spirit baggage of her husband?

Fukami: That's correct. The reverse can also take place, however. It's for that reason that marriage can be scary. To decide on a spouse simply on the basis of a physical impression can lead to all kinds of complications. I would like to offer a bit of advice to any couple thinking of getting married. They should consider three factors. First, they should carefully look at their partner's family background. This is to determine whether they have a good chance to stay together. What about the parents, brothers and sisters and their spouses? How about other relatives? Even if some of these married couples might have separated for a time but returned together, then there should be no problem. With the average marriage there is absolutely no need to worry and the prospects are good. However, if one of the future in-laws is talented and financially set but has already been married and divorced three or four times, then the couple should see warning lights. In other words, their proposed marriage is ill-fated.

Yamamoto: You mean in cases where the parents or relatives of one of the couple have been repeatedly divorced?

Fukami: That's right. Again I would say that a woman should note whether or not her husband-to-be has a bright personality. Of course, a bright, healthy character is one thing a woman should be looking for in a husband. If a man is very cheery, it is unlikely that he has any deep, dark karmic past. And of course you're not likely to find many bright, depressed men, or many bright, cold types. It stands to reason that if a person is outgoing, he is likely to be warm and straightforward. What this boils down to really is that if a person is cheerful he came from a good part of the spirit world. Even if such a person has a slight bit of karmic baggage to tote around, he should be able to get rid of it eventually. So, think of bright men as suitable marriage partners.

Patient Perseverance Is a Must

Fukami: This is one of the factors that is most important in a marriage partner. But don't think that I'm saying that if a man is just bright and cheerful, defects should be over-looked...now the third factor to consider is whether the man has held down a steady job for ten years or more. Too many men get bored or tired with their work. In terms of love that's the equivalent of the type of guy who tires of his woman after only a few years. But if a man stays at the same firm for a decade or more, it is an indication that he has willpower. Call it strength of character or stick-to-it-iveness. Even if this kind of man grows a bit tired of marriage, he does not dream of walking out on his wife; instead he looks for ways to preserve the relationship and work things out with her. He does not view the changing of marriage partners as being such a simple matter. On the other hand, find a man who is always changing jobs and personal interests, and you'll see that he is also more likely than not skipping from one wife to the next. This kind of fellow should never be considered as a prospective marriage partner. Whether or not a man keeps the same job and interests for ten years or more – this should be one of the major criteria in judging whether he is fit for marriage.

Takayama: But most Japanese get married while they are in their 20s. Few people in that age bracket have been working for ten years or more.

Fukami: In that case you go back to their school days and see whether they belonged to any club or sports team and find out whether they stuck with one thing or were constantly flitting from this to that. The important thing is to see whether there is a pattern to sticking with something once it was started.

Takayama: It's certainly true that if a person does not have the willpower for the long haul, he or she is not likely to accomplish much of worth.

Fukami: That's exactly how it is. Many people have pointed this out. Human beings have one soul made up of four spirits or *mitama*. As to which is the most important, the 19th century thinker Hirata Kanetane declared decisively that it is the *aramitama*. Now the chief characteristics of the *aramitama* are courage and perseverance, depending on whether you are talking about outward action or internal action. Besides the *aramitama*, we also have the *kushimitama*, *nigimitama* and *sakimitama*. The *kushimitama* manifests itself in the form of wisdom or intelligence, the *nigimitama* in the form of harmony and cooperation and the *sakimitama* in the form of love. Among these four spirits, Hirata believed the *aramitama*, as represented by the quality of perseverance, to be the most important. And that is really true. For even if you have intelligence, love and are the epitome of cooperation, if you cannot keep these things going for you for at least a year, then you will accomplish absolutely nothing. Since human beings are born of flesh and blood, it is only natural that we should experience suffering at times. It is only if you have the persistence to outlast these hard times that you will be able to make anything of yourself in this material world. So I would advise women when they are choosing a marriage partner to pay particularly close attention to the *aramitama*. Does the man exhibit courage, perseverance and fortitude? Those are the things to be looking for.

Karma From Past Lives and the Question of Marriage

Yamamoto: What happens in a case like mine? What if a girl has decided she would like to get married and has found a suitable partner who has the three qualifications that you spoke of? But what if as in my case my partner's mother has been bedridden for several years, his younger brother suddenly becomes very ill and dies, and one misfortune after the next attacks his family? Can a girl in shoes like mine go ahead and get married?

Fukami: At the very least, it's hard to promise that she will be happy. However, if we're talking merely about luck in marriage, it wouldn't necessarily be poor. She and her husband might form an ideal couple. Of course, if we are blessed with health and wealth, any talents that we might be endowed with are only added blessings. Anyhow, when you get down to it, a good marriage is really the most important thing. But no matter how much money you may have, or how good your health might be, if your husband is playing around all the time, you're never going to be happy.

Takayama: You find a lot of people in that situation too.

Fukami: Nevertheless, even if a person is perplexed as to whether or not she should marry, she should be thankful for her good fortune. A lot of women don't even have a chance to get married. Recently I talked with such an unlucky person. She said, "Mr. Fukami, people who have good sexual karma are really lucky. I don't have a man or any sexual karma at all, it would seem. Even if I had to suffer for it, I wish I could have a relationship with a man." There are many people like that.

Takayama: Looking at things from that perspective, at least you are better off than such unfortunates.

Yamamoto: No, that's not really true. I just want stability now. I'm just sick of all the trouble I've had.

Fukami: As I've said many times, those problems are the result of the vengeful spirits that have been attacking the Kato and Yamamoto families for several generations. But the reason why you have survived so well until today despite these awful conditions is that your guardian spirits have stood by you. And when you reach twenty-five, your guardian spirits will change. After that everything will change completely too.

Yamamoto: Three years ago when I had my palm read by one of Japan's foremost fortune tellers, he said exactly the same thing – age twenty-five would be a turning point in my life. The fact is I'm twenty-five now. Maybe this really is a fundamental turning point in my life. But everything is so terrible now, that I doubt that this is really that turning point.

Fukami: It is that turning point. From now on things in your life will start to get beautiful.

Yamamoto: Twenty-five years old is supposed to be a lucky time. So this year should be good to me. But still I can't help but wonder...

Fukami: You'll find good fortune. It is only because the current of your fate is flowing so turbulently at the moment that we can talk so frankly like this.

Takayama: Your fortune is changing tremendously even at this very moment.

Yamamoto: Is that really true?

Fukami: You fell in love when you were twenty-one, didn't you? And you were hurt badly by that affair. And thereafter you kept stumbling around. Fruitless love after fruitless love, you kept chasing after shadows. A dead-end street.

Yamamoto: That's the way it was. But, but, how could you know all that?

Fukami: It's because I can read your subconscious. Of course, I verify what I detect with your guardian spirits. But the reason why you were frustrated so often was that the spirits threw obstacles in your way. Any chance at a successful romance was destroyed by the 20-meter-long snake that was stalking you.

Yamamoto: This year more than any time before I thought I would finally make it. But it looks like failure again.

Fukami: Next autumn when you are twenty-six everything will finally work itself out. But you still have to be very, very careful. You were born into a family with a heavy karmic history. To put it bluntly, in a previous life you were a major warrior. Moreover, he had five concubines to wait on him. That's because he only could enjoy himself when he was pitting one person against another.

Yamamoto: Ah, I have that tendency inside me too.

Fukami: That means you tend to enjoy forcing men to compete against one another.

Yamamoto: Yes. I have to admit it. It's nothing to laugh at, but I really have to admit I have that particular personality trait within me. But how do you know that too? You amaze me. Even though I don't really want to be like that, why should it be that I end up acting that way?

Fukami: That's what I'm saying, it's the legacy of your karmic past. The five concubines you kept in your previous life were forced to compete among themselves to see whose child would be recognized as heir and suffered terribly as a result. The seeds that were sown then have grown wild since. You have to know that two of those five concubines committed suicide. The karma of that previous age is still alive today. Only this time around it is you who is being made to suffer at the hands of men.

Yamamoto: It seems I'm always suffering.

Fukami: And it always ends up the same, doesn't it? You say to yourself, "I've been betrayed. It's so vexing. I hoped that I would be treated tenderly. That's all I really wanted. And now I end up like this again. I'll never trust a man again. But I still have to get married."

You're torn by these conflicting emotions. Distrust. Hate. Distress. But still in your heart you won't give up on love. You're caught in this swamp with no way out...

Yamamoto: You put it well.

Fukami: But it's really your own fault. The legacy of previous lives continues and you are susceptible to being swept along by the tide. That tendency will continue until you are around thirty-five. So you have to be constantly on your guard.

Yamamoto: Could you be specific. How are these things going to show up?

Fukami: For example, one year after you get married, when you are twenty-seven, there will be chances with other men,

Yamamoto: Won't I really have a chance to get married when I turn twenty-six?

Fukami: That'll be about the time you can start thinking seriously about it. But I should warn you that when you're twenty-seven, twenty-nine and thirty-three, things will be dangerous for you. After you're married you will meet various men. And even though you'll simply want to have a no-strings-attached affair, you'll end up being the one who is in over her head and who gets burned. For example, if you become pregnant, the man is likely to run away. You might find yourself saying to yourself, "Oh, what on earth can I do? If my husband finds out, I'll be done for. Why should it be that I always end up blue like this?" You might find yourself with your back up against the wall like this. But just remember, it's your own fault. In a past life you did the same kind of thing to other women. So it's only natural that this kind of fate should befall you. So, like I say, be on your guard. Give up once and for all any thought of illicit affairs.

Yamamoto: Can I do that with sufficient will power?

Fukami: Definitely yes. If a guy comes over trying to pick you up, just tell him, "The truth is I have a dangerous disease." Keep him at a distance from the start. If you handle things that way, he's not going to try to get any nearer. You're going to have these kinds of problems until you are thirty-three or so. So be on the alert. With enough will power, enough gumption, you can overcome these problems.

Yamamoto: I take it you are referring not to spirit power but to my own will power?

Fukami: Exactly. Will power is the key here. But as I've said over and over again, it's oh so easy for you to slip and follow the tendencies built into you from previous lives. You really have to concentrate all the resolve you possibly can. Among other things, don't let yourself get involved in love triangles.

Karma and Happiness in This Life

Takayama: But love triangles and other similar abnormal situations are not all caused by the influence of spirits, are they?

Fukami: No, they're not. Some are certainly caused by the meddling of unfriendly spirits, but others are the product of karma from a past life.

Takayama: In Ms. Yamamoto's case, the problem can be traced to karma from a past life, can't it?

Fukami: Yes, it is rooted in karma from a past life. In her case the innate way of thinking that governs her actions are more or less the result of her ties to a previous life, karma, fate or however you want to label them. If you were to strip away the various spiritual obstacles caused by this link to the past, then you would be left with her individual karma. If through force of will she can change that, then she could also improve the karma left over from past lives.

Takayama: Does that mean that individuals who from the start do not have a very strong individual karmic link to the past and whose family baggage from the past is also light, don't have to make a very great effort to attain happiness?

Fukami: To be frank, that's exactly how things stand. For example, occasionally you see couples who are cheating on their spouses, though not having conceived any children are able to make a clean break without much fuss, or couples who were more or less coerced into marriage, but end up enjoying a very happy married life. Such people are very lucky. But people who have a heavy karmic load to bear or whose families have important unresolved business from the past cannot get off so easily. In the end, everything goes against them and they always end up unhappy.

Takayama: Well, then. It would seem that if you look at the results in a person's life, you can more or less tell what his or her individual and family karma is.

Fukami: That's right, it's easy to figure these things out. It's difficult to try to understand what has happened by looking at the process, but very easy to judge from the results. In other words, if a person seems to enjoy happiness no matter what he does, then the karmic influences and legacy of the past are insignificant. Conversely, chronic unhappiness is a sign that they are greatly influencing the person's life.

Takayama: So if the influence of the past is slight, then no matter what a person does, things are likely to come out all right.

Fukami: No, not necessarily. True, if karmic influences are not important, then in general things will tend to go well. However, you have to remember that the basic reason human beings are born is to improve their *mitama*, to lift them up to a higher spiritual level. If a person forgets this fundamental law and devotes himself solely to self-gratification, sometime or another he is going to have to pay for it. You see we're basically drawing on "cash boxes" from our previous lives. If we use our capital up, then we are in effect using our happiness up. So a person who is only concerned with his own pleasure may have a very enjoyable life, only to find that in his twilight years he tumbles down into the pits. And when he is reborn the next time, he will have to grow up among very harsh conditions. No matter how much we might try to avoid it in the end our actions will be accounted for in the tally book of karma.

Sexual Pitfalls

Takayama: This is related to an earlier question. Are all troubles and unhappiness in male-female relations the result of sexual karma?

Fukami: No, not all of them. Rather you might say that an absence of friction is an indication that sexual karma is operating strongly in the relationship.

Takayama: Really? How could that be?

Fukami: Well, for example, sometimes you run across a real beauty, who has a terrific sense of style. But for some reason or other, she seems to have a melancholy air about her that scares men away. That kind of isolated individual often has no trouble at all with members of the opposite sex, but he or she is plagued by lustful karma. Homosexuals and lesbians are in the same situation. The same holds true for people who are overly squeamish about heterosexual relations.

Takayama: In other words, it's a kind of overcompensation.

Fukami: Yes, you grasped my point perfectly. That's exactly what it is. People who in their past life led a life of debauchery received very severe punishment in the spirit world after they died. After they had undergone a change of heart and were reborn, many of them – assuming they are men – say they want nothing more to do with women. They develop a real complex against male-female relations. You might call it a reaction.

Takayama: Nevertheless, society tends to think that having no sexual problems is in itself something very laudable.

Fukami: True, it sounds good at first. But when things seem too proper, almost without fail it is a sign that the seeds of unhappiness have already been scattered.

Takayama: What is the most intense facet of sexual karma?

Fukami: I'd have to say it is the wandering spirits of women who in the past were sold into brothels. The wrath of women who were deceived by men, sold to brothel keepers and then forced against their will to be professional playthings for men is about as extreme a manifestation of sexual links to the past that you can find. In the spirit world all of them have taken on the form of snakes: pitch black snakes. Snakes with horns on their heads. And they do not undergo any change of heart whatsoever. Next in order of intense feeling are the girls who were sold to brothels by their parents. These women too are consumed with violent passions. Even though they said constantly to themselves, "It can't be helped; it is for the sake of my beloved parents," still after ten, twenty or even thirty years of shame, though they continued to say "It can't be helped," inside their hearts they came to detest their parents. Of course there are individual differences in this regard, but in most of the cases that I have seen these women have come to revile their parents. Still, those prostitutes who were sold into white slavery by the man they loved are the most obsessed of all.

Takayama: So such a woman seeks revenge not only against the man who betrayed her, but his descendants as well?

Fukami: That's generally how things work. However, in cases where the woman was treated in especially inhuman fashion, it is not unusual to see the brothel keeper also become a target of revenge.

Takayama: How is this thirst for vengeance expressed?

Fukami: Nearly always through love affairs. These can continue on down through the generations.

Takayama: What form exactly do they take?

Fukami: Involvement may be with a man with a wife and children. Or the woman may get hooked on a man of the lowest sort and be plunged into unhappiness. Usually, she runs off with a real rogue, who not only refuses to do a lick of work, but forces her to support him, even while he beats, kicks and batters her on a regular basis. If she runs away from the brute and gets a divorce, it really doesn't matter, because she'll soon get involved with another guy of the same sort. Only it will be worse this time. He'll make her work in a massage parlor as a prostitute. There can be no doubt in such cases that either the vengeful spirit of a long dead prostitute or a fox spirit is at work. Or even a band of spirits – a family that was massacred sometime in the past.

Yamamoto: I know people with stories like that. Would those people also be the target of vengeful spirits?

Fukami: I should think so. Take the case of a woman who before marriage thinks her fiancé the finest man on earth, only to discover afterwards that all he's interested in is gambling at the bicycle and horse races and other women. On top of that he manhandles her all the time. The reason why she has to suffer in such a relationship is as I explained before that spirits are out to make her pay for something she or her ancestors did. They want her to taste the same agony and maltreatment that they did. That agony is their revenge.

Takayama: Are women the only ones who become possessed?

Fukami: No, not at all. Men can be afflicted too. All members of these families are targets for possession by these vengeful spirits.

Takayama: When a man becomes the target, what form does the possession take?

Fukami: Let me offer an example. There are women who before marriage appear to be as sweet as can be. But almost as soon as they leave the altar, they turn into first class drunkards or gamblers and cause their husbands enormous suffering as they lead them down into the lowest depths of a living hell. In the worst cases they chase their husbands around with knives. A man who has the misfortune to marry a woman of this kind no doubt had an ancestor who was a brothel keeper and caused countless women untold suffering. Or maybe that ancestor took advantage of a maid, thereby causing her to commit suicide. Or maybe he whipped her and treated her so cruelly that she took sick and died. Such cases are frequent. But still in the majority of cases, the wrath of a female spirit is directed against a female of the household. Get her to marry a worthless punk, and then the unfortunate and her family can taste the cup of anguish that the spirit knows so well. Nothing gives these vengeful female spirits greater satisfaction. Such cases are definitely in the majority.

Takayama: So these are the most virulent of the vengeful spirits with some kind of sexual connection?

Fukami: That's right. However, I should note that in this same general field of sexually connected troubles there are people whose problems are due to their own individual karma.

Takayama: Due to individual karma?

Fukami: Yes, the person's own karma derived from actions in past lives is the root cause of the problem in such cases. For example, everyone else in the family might have made a happy marriage, but this one person has not found a husband. You see this kind of thing all the time. Although her younger sisters all have splendid husbands, the oldest daughter alone has no luck. Why should she be saddled with a boyfriend who does nothing but hit the bottle and doesn't know the meaning of the word work? On top of that she's borne his children. Finally, she breaks off from the guy, thinking to herself, "At last I'm free." Soon, however, she is involved with a real gangster type. When things like that happen, you have to think that it is not just a case of the family's ties to the past, there is also a heavy dose of personal karma involved that allows influences from earlier lives to shape the individual's current existence on earth. This woman no doubt caused men to suffer in a previous existence, so now this time around the tables have been turned on her. Of course, even in such cases, usually there are vengeful spirits involved too. Many times you will also find ancestors who have been condemned to the hell of lust teaming up in an alliance with these vengeful spirits.

Guardian Spirits Reinforce Willpower

Yamamoto: Previously you said that my chances for marriage will increase from the time I reach twenty-six. Will my future marriage partner be a man I know now?

Fukami: Well, let me put it this way, there's about a 65% chance that things will work out that way.

Yamamoto: The person I have in mind is a married man, but...

Fukami: Wow, why is it you always end up heading in the same direction? Probably because you followed the exact same pattern in your previous life. I tell you, it's not good for you at all. You better change your ways.

Yamamoto: Maybe so....But I can't give him up....

Takayama: In this situation doesn't it seem like this pattern is due to the fact that her karma has caused her to be deluded by a spirit that keeps dragging her in a direction she shouldn't be going?

Fukami: In such cases a spirit is often responsible. However, if the individual is stronger than the spirit, then he or she won't be led astray.

Takayama: When you speak of strength, are you referring to will power?

Fukami: Yes. But when I speak of will power, don't get the idea that it just wells up out of nowhere. Will power is the end result of study, training and the right kind of faith. These are the foundation stones of real will power. For example, if some kind of temptation suddenly arises due to sexual ties with the past, a person who has will power will simply declare to himself or herself, "No, stop. Go ahead and do this and you will just be starting on the road to your own ruin. Stop right here." People can do that if they have built up will power based on education, training and faith. In other words, they will have that reserve ability that allows them to escape from tight spots.

Takayama: You mean it's advisable to acquire knowledge as a means of getting a handle on your emotions?

Fukami: That's right. In that way, people who have developed will power backed up by correct knowledge will be able to deal with their feelings. In turn, their guardian spirits will do everything possible to protect them from harm. Consequently, even evil spirits will not bother such a person. On the other hand, people who are governed by their passions are easy targets for those spirits. In the case of vengeful spirits, these weak individuals are the ones they are most likely to go after. To put it simply, if you build up your will power and learn to rely on your guardian spirits, then you have nothing to worry about. An evil spirit will look at you and say to itself, "This one's too strong for me." Then it will head off on its own way.

Yamamoto: But aren't there many cases in which people find true happiness by divorcing and then remarrying another person?

Fukami: If your thinking is based on an objective evaluation of his situation and your own capabilities and temperament, then there may be some basis for your reasoning. But if we're merely dealing with emotions here, I advise you to break this relationship off just as soon as possible. If sublime spiritual feelings are involved, that's one thing. But if you're being tossed about by feelings of passion and lust, then you are headed for disaster and self-destruction and there will be no escape from that course. In the end, you and your partner will both end up profoundly unhappy. That's exactly what will happen if you give way to those kinds of feelings. Just remember there are evil spirits in the background, pulling strings to lead you towards your doom through the vehicle of your own emotions.

Yamamoto: Still aren't there many exceptions to what you have been talking about. Many people divorce, get remarried and live a very happy life.

Fukami: No matter what I advise, you seem determined to go in that direction. If so, better have the guy divorce his wife as soon as possible. But even though he promises over and over that he will separate from her, he probably intends to string things out as long as possible.

Takayama: That's it. If your "man" had already made a clean break with his spouse, then we'd be talking about a totally different situation, but....

Yamamoto: That's true, but....Sometimes I think I'll give up on him and break it off. Other times I want to hold on a bit longer. All kinds of thoughts go through my brain. I've gotten so confused.

Fukami: Why don't you just give him a clear deadline? Say to him, "Please get divorced within this year. If you don't, then we'll just have to break up." If this man has any sense of sincerity at all, he'll give you a clear answer.

Yamamoto: But, he still cares for his wife too. If their marriage was totally lacking in feeling that would be one thing, but they still care for each other. For example, his wife is very ill, so he just can't go and divorce her like that right now...

Takayama: That's the kind of line a guy like that would give.

Yamamoto: But I know he's not lying. He'd never lie. At least I don't think he ever would....assuming what he says is true. In that case I'm thinking that it would make sense for us to set a time limit for us calling it quits....

Fukami: If what this man is saying is true, then he is totally lacking in moral courage and true love. Look, his wife is supposed to be seriously ill. Now what if he just dumps her, leaves her for you. Don't you think his wife will be pitiful. Looking at things from the point of your own happiness, I'd say dragging this thing out is just pointless.

Takayama: A guy like that will end up doing the same thing to you if you go ahead and marry him.

Fukami: That's right. He is not the right kind of marriage partner for you. So you should screw up your courage and say to him, "When I think about your wife, it's clear that it would be better for you to stay with your family than to marry me. That's where your true happiness lies. So please forget about me." Make a clean break of it. It will be better for both of you in the long run.

Yamamoto: Let's take a case where spirits are involved. After a spiritual purification, does a person's heart suddenly feel lightened and that person suddenly say to himself or herself, "Ah, it's over."

Fukami: Well, it becomes easier for that to happen.

Yamamoto: Well, I was clinging to such a hope that that would happen and that's why I came to you.

Fukami: I can see that.

Takayama: Sometimes these things can hurt so bad it seems unbearable.

Fukami: It may hurt, but it has to be seen through to the end.

Takayama: If only the will power inside of you can be brought out.

Fukami: That's right. Because remember there are spirits that are constantly seeking to pull you in the opposite direction.

Yamamoto: If those spirits can be exorcised, does that mean that I will become free?

Fukami: Definitely. But things are really that simple only in cases in which the spirits have had possession of a person for a comparatively short length of time – say a week or month. Getting rid of spirits tied to one locality or wandering ghosts is a fairly simple task. But when a spirit has possessed a person for a year, ten years or a similar long period of time, or when on top of that the type of possession is especially vehement, then even if you conduct a spiritual purification, you can't be sure that at that place and time everything will be turned completely around. Many times things do work out all right. But generally things are rather difficult.

Yamamoto: Why is that?

Fukami: Well, let me compare it to magnetism. Think of yourself as being affected by a kind of magnetism. If you place a magnet next to some iron for 30 minutes or an hour and then remove it there will be little or no residual effect. But if you leave them in contact for a week, a month, or more, then even when you remove the magnet, you will find that the iron has retained some magnetic properties. We're dealing with a situation that is very similar. So with a person who has been bewitched by spirits for many years, you can be sure that they have been greatly influenced by these spirits – in their thinking and personal attributes. In a sense these evil spirits have wormed their way into the person's character and very soul.

Takayama: That means that after a spiritual purification you cannot expect any immediate...

Fukami: Correct, things can't be turned around just like that. The echoes of the scarring experience remain behind.

Yamamoto: Then what needs to be done?

Fukami: You have to pray to your guardian spirits with all of your might and seek to build up your will power. That's all you can do. You pray for the support of benevolent spirits and at the same time try your utmost to bolster your own self will. If you can get the positive magnetism of your group of guardian spirits to back you up then in a comparatively short period of time you can recover. Unless you struggle to eliminate that lingering echo and the residual negative magnetism you will continue to wallow in the snake pit of negative emotions.

Yamamoto: Can I do that on my own?

Fukami: If you earnestly ask your guardian spirits for their support, explain what you are trying to do and promise that you will also do your part to become stronger.

Takayama: By saying these things inside our hearts can we communicate with our guardian spirits?

Fukami: No, you have to say them clearly out loud. There's a ten-fold difference in power between saying them silently in the heart and speaking them out loud. That is to say, enunciating them clearly is ten times more effective. For that reason, any time you are praying – not just to your guardian spirits – you get much better results if you speak out loud. That goes for saying prayers at Shinto shrines or praying to the Buddhas as well. Avoid silent prayer. Ms. Yamamoto, you must speak out clearly and say something like, "I promise to break with that man within the week." Repeat it over and over again. That is the way to convince your guardian spirits of your new resolve.

Yamamoto: I see.

Fukami: Still, don't think that if you do that you'll be able to achieve a sudden breakthrough in your life and resolve all your problems. Things are never that easy. In such cases things tend to be messy. If you finally decide to call it quits with this guy, you'll undoubtedly still get calls from him, and he'll plead, "Why are you doing this to us?"

Yamamoto: That's sure to happen.

Fukami: He'll give you a sob story. Maybe something like this:

"I'm so sad. You know last night I went to a bar and sat there weeping." If you ask, "Is that really true?" He may break down right there on the phone. Should that old phone start ringing off the hook right after you have finally made up your mind, you can be sure it's all the work of those vengeful spirits. Everything will be better after you've received the salvation of spiritual purification. But when he stays in touch, you may come to think, "Ah, even though I tried my hardest to break this thing off, it seems like I can't really get away from him." Then you may deceive yourself into thinking that your relationship is a matter of fate. But be advised that even though you may have gotten rid of your demons, you may still be plagued by his own.

Brother + Sister = Lovers

Yamamoto: Well, continuing with my story. I have to admit that when I am with this man I feel somehow strangely happy and satisfied.

Fukami: If you want me to tell you the downright truth: in an earlier existence you two were brother and sister.

Yamamoto: What! Really? Somehow I felt that myself before. Honestly, we have so many things in common.

Fukami: He was your older brother.

Yamamoto: Yes, I can believe it. I keep wondering how two people can possibly be so compatible. I could never imagine that someone so like me could possibly appear in my life. When we are together it is like heaven on earth, as if we were one. Every minute, every second.

Fukami: That's because you were brother and sister in a previous existence. But you have to learn to control yourself. You can be

169

friends, but leave the sex alone. Control your emotions. Remember his poor wife.

Yamamoto: Still, that guy seems so unhappy. His mother is bedridden. And then his father suddenly passed away. Now his wife has tuberculosis. And his child has infantile asthma.

Fukami: Then you should be able to see that the karmic connections of the entire family are similar to yours.

Yamamoto: Yes, I can see that. We're all so miserable.

Fukami: The karmic connections of your families are alike and you've become intertwined. But all that means is that you are both going to be dragged further in a negative direction. I can see it all so clearly. Among other things there is a more than 20-meter-long snake, incorporating the spirit of that band of vengeful *samurai*; and it has cursed you all and possessed the entire Yamamoto family. And there is a similar band that laid a curse on his family generations ago. And these two groups gather together in the spirit world sometimes. "Ah, friends you have a vendetta to consummate, do you? Truth to tell, so do we." "Let us join forces then and damn these two." "So it shall be. So it shall be." You and he have sworn to be as one even unto death, have you not? That's their dirty work.

Yamamoto: That's how it is.

Fukami: In many cases like this, you see the lovers taking a vow that should they both fall ill they will commit suicide together. Under all this psychological pressure and suffering, if one of the lovers falls ill and cannot recover, that person will think that he or she no longer wants to bear the unhappiness of this life. Only death holds any attraction. And looking into that person's eyes, the partner will say, "I too feel that way. It seems to be our fate." And then the two will walk the road of death together. Call it suicide if you like. But it is really assassination by the Murder Incorporated formed in the spirit world between those two bands of vengeful spirits. I know all of this defies belief. It sounds like nonsense. But every word is the truth.

Takayama: Do such joint suicides really occur?

Fukami: They do happen and as the result of the cooperation between spirits seeking their own vengeance against one of the partners.

Takayama: Is this true for the *shinju*, love suicides, that we hear so much about in Japanese tradition?

Fukami: In many cases yes. That's because both of the people involved are cursed by bad karma and when these two karmas are joined together the result is disaster. Ms. Yamamoto, if things continue as they are, you'll become ill and unable to move the lower half of your body. You'll lay in bed at home and think, "Oh, death would be better than a life like this." That's what you'll think, I guarantee you. And then you'll consider gassing yourself to death. You've already decided that the proper way to die for you should be suicide by gas, haven't you?

Yamamoto: Yes, I want to go happily. I thought that gas would be best.

Fukami: Gas has an evil smell, so you first would swallow a batch of sleeping pills and then turn on the gas spigot, and then everything would be so pleasurable. You would just float off....You could see the beautiful image before you....But the evil spirits were doing this to you, I tell you. They wanted to put that image in your mind so they could kill you.

Yamamoto: It's true. Recently, I have thought there's nothing left for me but to die. I seem so indifferent to life. Somehow I seem to lack the tenacity to hang on to life.

Takayama: Those spirits want you to think in that fashion.

Yamamoto: Maybe that's so. Really, I swear I'm not exaggerating for effect. I just want to seek relief, release. I just want to sleep so. But Fukami-san, how can you know all this?

Fukami: It's because I tuned into the wavelength of the vengeful spirits that are after you – read their minds, so to speak.

Takayama: Uh!

Fukami: The man I spoke about before we began this discussion. The man who killed himself with pesticide. He was in a similar situation.

Yamamoto: This is really scary.

Fukami: The vengeful spirits have an agenda of their own. First they bring trouble to your life. Then they make you ill. Finally they convince you that you want to end it all. They have their little scenario all figured out from the start. These spirits aren't fools, you know. They were generals when they were alive.

Takayama: What Mr. Fukami is trying to get at now is that those spirits can hear it all. Still he's saying this all on purpose. It sounds like he's half trying to persuade them.

Emotional People Are Especially Susceptible

Yamamoto: Is it easier for these vengeful spirits to take possession of men or women?

Fukami: It doesn't really matter. They'll possess either one. But I'd have to say that women usually prove easier targets for possession. The reason is that generally speaking women are more emotional. Most women think with their hearts instead of their heads.

Takayama: Are emotional men also easy targets?

Fukami: Yes, they are. Emotional men of weak will, the sick and debilitated, compassionate, tender-hearted types – these are the kinds of men who are in most danger.

Takayama: It follows then that strong-willed men must prove difficult targets.

Fukami: Definitely so. Strong-willed men who have a stubborn streak in them, give off spiritual vibrations – a kind of brilliance of the soul – that drives the evil spirits away. They take one look at this kind of man and say to themselves, "No use fooling with this guy." In other words, if you want to avoid becoming a target of these spirits, you should establish clear goals and then undeviatingly strive all out to accomplish them. In the spirit world the power of strong will power is a sword of spirit power and majesty. The core spirits of such men literally give off a brilliant light that spreads out around them. They have an inner power that flows out from their person and prevents evil forces from even approaching them.

Takayama: I see.

Fukami: You're feeling better now, aren't you?

Yamamoto: Yes, I am.

Fukami: Your ancestors who committed suicide, that old man we were talking about and other spirits affecting you heard what we were saying and doubts were thereby raised in their minds and each asked himself or herself, "Why really did I kill myself?" After this self-revelation, they left your body.

Not All Spiritual Obstacles Are Bad

Takayama: But Fukami-san, during these spiritual purifications you certainly seem to exhaust yourself.

Fukami: I won't deny that. But it's not really all that bad. As I mentioned earlier, a spiritual purification on one hand requires one's own strength. But basically you have to rely on outside power; in other words you have to pray for the help of the gods. The master of spiritual purification's power in itself is inadequate.

Takayama: Yes, I can see how that would be.

Fukami: At the same time, I have to admit that it is not something easy to do. Every single day I'm struggling with the evil forces in the negative spirit world. And it takes its toll. If I'm out enjoying some beautiful natural sights and then my psychic powers detect a floating evil spirit roaming about the area, it really disgusts me. This type of thing causes a great deal of unhappiness to psychics like myself.

Yamamoto: Can you actually see them out there?

Fukami: Only if I want to. That's why I usually switch that psychic channel to the off position, so I don't have to see those things. However, during a spiritual purification I have to see it all. There are things I would rather not see. Say I see an incredibly beautiful woman, but then look into her inner world and find out she has had an abortion. That kind of thing distresses me. Looking upon the face of her soul, I cannot help but feel intense disappointment.

Takayama: Can you really see things so clearly?

Fukami: Yes, I can see them. If I really want to. Behind the face of every person I see is a long line of other faces; faces of people that he or she has been involved with.

So if I say, "Didn't a former lover of yours have long eyebrows, narrow eyes and say things like this..." people will inevitably cry, "Yes, but how could you possibly know?" The truth is that the guardian spirits show me these things. Actually, things are slightly more complicated than that. Sometimes the person's guardian spirit will show me, sometimes I will be able to see into the depths of the person's subconscious, and sometimes my own guardian spirits will reveal it to me. There are several different ways in which I can get this knowledge.

Takayama: Is this connected to the concept of spiritual telepathy that you wrote about in your book *Divine Powers?*

Fukami: Yes, this spiritual telepathy – or reading of other people's hearts – is used in conjunction with the spiritual power of Heaven's eye. Since by employing this concept of spiritual telepathy I can get inside another person's thoughts, I am able to win the confidence of the people I advise and provide them with the right counsel. That's because I can peer right inside their souls without any obstructions whatsoever. Without this clear perspective on things, it would be impossible for me to render proper advice like I did earlier to Ms. Yamamoto. I would just have to talk in circles, trying to hit the nail on the head. Recently, however, the opportunities to use such powers in this way have diminished somewhat....

Takayama: This is really amazing. Of course, you, Mr. Fukami, might be privy to all these secrets, but these are things that people like myself know absolutely nothing about. We can't possibly know whether or not a certain situation or phenomenon has been caused by spirits. Do you have any certain methods to decide whether they are involved or not?

Fukami: Yes, I do. Actually, anyone is capable of discerning such involvement if they very carefully observe various phenomena. For example, if the same pattern keeps showing up over and over, you can be certain that there are spirits at work. If the girlfriend you had before suddenly died of illness. And then you found out that your next lover had a husband and everything fell apart. If this kind of pattern keeps repeating itself over and over, you should accept the fact that some spirit or other has it out for you. As a rule of thumb, if the same pattern is repeated two or three times, it indicates a spirit is around.

Yamamoto: Are there such cases in which there is no spirit involvement?

Fukami: Yes. There are many cases in which the careless attitude or arrogance of the individual, or his own personal karma from past lives lies at the root of the problem. But the number of instances in which there is absolutely no influence from the spirit world are minimal. In a complementary role, to a greater or lesser degree – almost always there is some kind of influence by the spirits. Sometimes these spirits are evil, but sometimes they are out to do good. Some are strong; some are weak. Think of it as a flux between periods of good influence and periods of evil influence – an endless rivalry between good and evil.

Takayama: You speak about involvement by good spirits. Could you give some examples?

Fukami: Well, usually they don't make their presence known at all. They simply foster tranquillity and safety. When the guardian spirits are on strict guard and the person does not have such bad karma, then an atmosphere of tranquillity, safety and harmony will prevail around him or her. So this kind of atmosphere is the ultimate that we should be aiming for in our lives. And when we have it, we need to express our heartfelt gratitude to the gods and our guardian spirits.

Takayama: But aren't such people who enjoy true tranquillity and peace of mind few and far between?

Fukami: There aren't many, I'd have to admit. Nearly everyone has problems of one sort or another.

Takayama: But there do tend to be extremes. Some people seem to have all the cares of the world on their shoulders, while others rarely experience problems.

Fukami: That's true. They vary in number and intensity. However, even if a person has his share of problems, that is not necessarily something to be sad about. Many people going around sighing, "Why is it just me? Why should I always be so unhappy and blue?" But such self-pity is not at all good. If a person is always thinking like that, his mountain of troubles will just continue to grow and grow. Even when things seem to be going all wrong, you must not give up. Rather you should through sheer force of will power pull yourself forward and make that extra ounce of effort. If you do so, you will attract good fortune to yourself. Of course, the question is how to set about doing that. One method I suggest for exhibiting strength of will and pushing the *aramitama* to the fore is to build up the muscles. Aesthetic sensibilities are connected with the *kushimitama*, feelings are associated with the *sakimitama*, the internal organs are connected with the *nigimitama*, and the muscles and exterior of the body are associated with the *aramitama*. Exercise to train the muscles is something that regardless of whether it is done by men or women is something that is quite effective in demonstrating will power. Education, training, faith – all these things are difficult to maintain if our bodies are not in decent shape.

Takayama: But, oh how hard it is to get started...

Fukami: True. It certainly is hard to get started. However, once you get used to a training regimen, the whole process becomes interesting and you can observe yourself begin to change. And if you adopt a forward-looking, bright attitude and set out to overcome the obstacles in your path, your guardian spirits will lend you some of their spiritual strength, wisdom and good fortune. These things will offset and gradually wipe out the effects of karma and the suffering in your life. In ancient times, illustrious men all trained their bodies. That especially holds true for religious and political leaders. Many of them had past lives in which they picked up bad karma, but after once being condemned to hell, clawed their way back to this world to do good.

Takayama: I would never have imagined that. Condemned to hell. You mean some of these great men came to earth resembling a blank slate as far as karma is concerned?

Fukami: Of course some of these men had that kind of background. But it is difficult for that kind of person to lead other men. How can they know the worries and suffering of their fellow men? It's difficult to say whether those with deep ties to the past or those with shallow ties are really better off. People born into families with heavy karmic baggage simply have to overcome this family heritage. They refuse to be slaves to their inheritance, nor to be dragged here and there by hostile spirits from the negative spirit world.

Takayama: That's very interesting.

Fukami: And it is by persevering that such individuals are able to build up their characters. They build up their faith; they build up their knowledge; they build up their humanity. This is how great leaders or men of religion, men who lived for the sake of mankind became what they became. If you think of things in this way, karma might be thought of as a kind of manure for growth.

Takayama: Does that mean that people who do not have many difficult connections to earlier lives are destined to grieve?

Fukami: No, not at all. Such people with no great complications from earlier lives often bring into this life considerable merit which they accumulated in those earlier lives, which guarantees them a happy life this time around. And that's perfectly fine too. Nevertheless, someone who is happy all the time has a hard time empathizing with those who have more difficult karmic backgrounds and who are suffering in this life. So it is all but impossible for such individuals to become lay or religious leaders who can bring salvation to others. At the very least they won't be very capable masters of spiritual purifications.

Takayama: You mean those without difficult connections to previous lives cannot exorcise evil spirits?

Fukami: I won't say that it is impossible. Let's just say, very, very difficult. If they can bring to bear sufficient concentration of mind and soul and spiritual power, then that kind of person can also handle spiritual purifications. But if someone really desires to release the spirits from the traps they are caught in, he will have to have had the experience of suffering in hell sometime in one of his past lives, since only such an experience will make him capable of comprehending their suffering. Unless he can understand the full extent of the spirit's hatred and desire for revenge, no matter how often he may plead "Give up this vendetta," his message will simply fall on deaf ears. Occasionally however, when a person from a fortunate background through discipleship becomes a medium who conducts spiritual purifications, in order to let him fully understand the suffering that these vengeful spirits and ancestors rotting in hell are undergoing, his mentor may introduce an especially wild spirit, who will communicate this experience directly to him. This is referred to as "secret transmissions from vengeful spirits." Anyone who endures such an exceptional experience can become a first-class exorcist.

Takayama: Earlier you said that in olden times all the great leaders had overcome difficult relationships with previous lives. Is that really true?

Fukami: In talking about those men of old, I do not necessarily mean every single last man. But it is true for the greatest men. Some lost their wives. Others saw their children die. Some suffered from serious illnesses. They suffered one blow after the next. You can blame it on karma or spiritual obstacles placed in their path. But the important thing is that they did not let these things defeat them. Rather they accepted this suffering as a form of testing by Heaven and worked to overcome these difficulties.

Takayama: Why were great men of old able to do so?

Fukami: Because they had knowledge. But it wasn't the kind of rote memory and mental knowledge like we talk about today. It was knowledge about what it really means to be a human being. Men of old had this kind of knowledge, you know. For example, when they were undergoing tribulations, one after the next, they would turn to the Book of Mencius and read the passage, "When Heaven decides to entrust a man with an important task, he is made to suffer." This encouraged them to try harder.

In the same way Yoshida Shoin, one of the philosophical fathers of the Meiji Restoration, encouraged his disciples to read The Book of Mencius and to study books of the activist Wang Yang-ming School (Yomeigaku) of Confucianism. They were taught to consider all suffering as a form of spiritual testing. The followers of Yoshida went on to perform many meritorious deeds. Such men were in this manner able to overcome bad karma and spiritual obstacles and in fact turn them into something beneficial. And in the process they also established models for overcoming spiritual obstacles. Conversely, men who have not faced problems of karma and spiritual obstacles and who consequently have not had to go through such hard testing of themselves are not able to develop to their full height as a human being. Anyhow, this is the reason why I say that spiritual barriers are not necessarily bad.

After the Spiritual Purification

Takayama: If that kind of change comes about, then there shouldn't be any need for spiritual purifications.

Fukami: That's right. However, speaking from the standpoint of a psychic, if before my eyes I find a man or woman who is suffering, and is being tortured by a malevolent spirit, I could never stand aside and in detached manner advise, "You really should work this thing out by yourself." Such people are too pitiful. I undertake spiritual purifications precisely because I want to help these people and set the spirits free.

Yamamoto: Once a person undergoes a spiritual purification, does that mean that she will become free from illnesses and other spiritual hindrances?

Fukami: Sometimes recovery is prompt, sometimes it is not.

Takayama: What accounts for the difference?

Fukami: It depends on the type of possession involved, and the intensity of the hatred. It's impossible to make any blanket prediction. But one thing is clear. Those individuals who have been exorcised and then have experienced miraculous recoveries tend to be those who had wiped out some of their bad karma prior to the spiritual purification. Through their own effort they have wiped out some of the darkness. Sometimes they are not even aware of the fact themselves that they have weathered the worst of the storm and are constantly storing up spiritual merit. I have seen individuals who had suffered liver troubles for years be cured completely after a spiritual purification. It seemed like a lie. In many ways the process of spiritual purification might be regarded as a final push. That holds true when discussing the relationship with illness. After an especially vengeful spirit, the person who it had possessed often is extremely weak for some time. If viewed through a psychic's eyes, certain parts of the body appear to be dim and gloomy. These are spots where new spirits of all kinds have rushed in. In other words, sometimes when the person is down and out like that, another evil spirit will take advantage of the opportunity to enter his body. In such instances the individual gives the impression of not being at all well. Thereafter, spiritual purifications may have to be repeated on several occasions. If explained in medical or scientific terms, the lingering effects caused by spiritual hindrances might be attributed to rehabilitation taking place in the aura on that spot. When that finally occurs, then a quick recovery can take place. In addition, it should be emphasized that not all illnesses are caused by spiritual impediments even when you might think so. Some are due to curvature of the spine, some are the aftereffects of traffic accidents, others are simply the result of unhealthy habits. In such cases, spiritual barriers play absolutely no role. That is to say that spiritual hindrances are not the most significant cause of medical problems in all instances. In many cases however, after a person has undergone a spiritual purification he or she has been able to find a good hospital where the physical cause of the illness was discovered and treated. And thereafter the individual quickly achieved a complete recovery.

Takayama: That must be something of a shock for people who believed that spiritual purification can cure whatever ails them.

Fukami: With those who truly understand the principles involved there is no problem. After all there is no guarantee that even if you undergo a spiritual purification you will without fail immediately have a complete recovery. But think of it this way: even if there are not any immediate visible effects, in the spirit world itself the equivalent of a Copernican revolution is taking place. For that reason, if the person involved holds steady and true, then the spirits from the negative spirit world will no longer be able to have their way with him. Just remember the magnetism analogy I gave earlier. That person has been under the influence of these malevolent spirits for so long that he has become like that piece of magnetized iron. But time will heal in the spiritual sense and the negative influences will gradually dissipate.

Takayama: You have to let time take its course.

Fukami: Yes. There's no other way when an evil spirit has been in possession of the person for so long. Not too much attention should be paid to whether after the spiritual purification the illness heals right away or not. That's because the spirit already has departed for good. So I would tell people in that situation that it's best not to give a thought to those nasty spirits, but instead to throw themselves completely into their jobs or housework. Do so and before you know it you will be completely healed. Of course, sometimes people recover right off the bat.

Takayama: But that must happen rather seldom.

Fukami: True. These people often end up saying to themselves, "Somehow I still don't feel right; maybe it's an *Inari* fox or snake spirit." And often enough another evil spirit will have weaseled its way in by this time. Should that happen unfortunately, the person will have to undergo another spiritual purification. But even so, this second spiritual purification will only be half as effective as the first.

I'll have to be frank at this point and admit that when the karmic background is especially deep, there is an especially complicated, weird connection with past lives, or the spiritual hindrances are too much to overcome, the situation is different. In such cases, the one conducting the spiritual purification – be he a novice or the most powerful of veterans – may be helpless to get rid of the evil spirits no matter how many times he might try.

Takayama: What happens in such cases?

Fukami: I make a final attempt. I take the possessed person on a star tour to Pluto – the planet responsible for the severance of bad karmic ties. There I conduct a purification rite to deal with each of the major, direct links with past lives that are troubling the person and explain to him in detail the web of karma in which he is trapped. Then I conduct the spiritual purification.

Takayama: When you say you take people on a star tour....

Fukami: Of course, I don't physically transport their bodies – the corporal part of their being – to Pluto. What I do is take their *kushimitama* on a spiritual trip. I explain all of this in considerable detail in my book *Lucky Fortune.*

Takayama: That's absolutely incredible.

Fukami: I do it because it is the will of the gods, and because I consider it my responsibility. Actually, I don't even think that I am doing it myself. A special god really conducts these tours. I am just his vehicle to accomplish the mission. I can only describe this briefly, but you should know that not everyone is able to successfully be exorcised. There are many people who would like to undergo a spiritual purification, but they just are not right for it. They don't have the money for the *tamagushi* ritual present. Their parents oppose the whole notion. My schedule doesn't allow it. There are any number of reasons.

But the real reason that such spiritual purifications do not take place is that the god in charge has not given his approval. The gods and guardian spirits will not normally want to move against a spirit unless it is causing a real fuss. That is because in a spiritual sense a spiritual purification can be viewed as a kind of revenge against the spirit who is being shoved out of the person's body. If the possessed person does not indicate strong will power through fervid prayer to the gods, then he or she may lose the chance to have the evil spirit exorcised.

Takayama: I see. Looking at things that way, a spiritual purification is really one variety of miracle.

Fukami: It certainly is. It is an effort whose success remains at the mercy of the gods, a ritual cloaked in mystery. We as human beings may do everything possible to facilitate the success. But in the end everything is in the hands of the gods and Buddhas and we must follow their guidance and live by the special laws that govern the spirit world, such as karma. We can only pretend to have a very small understanding of the forces at work. But we can feel them in action, and we constantly find ourselves being surprised by how things work out.

CHAPTER 4

Secrets to Overcoming Karma
and the Spiritual Purification of the
Spirits of Aborted Babies

Overcoming Karma: the Ultimate Question

All human beings are under the influence of the spirits. They may be evil spirits or they may be well-meaning spirits. But you will find no one whose life is not being influenced by spirits. People who are strongly influenced by guardian spirits and other good spirits will find their happiness ever increasing. However, those people who unluckily are under the sway of vengeful spirits or other evil spirits, or who have even been possessed, will find themselves wallowing in misfortune. This being the way things are, it only makes sense to exert every possible effort not to become possessed by evil spirits. Likewise, those unfortunates who have already become possessed by such spirits need to be exorcised, exorcise themselves or take some other drastic measure to change their situation. Those have been the conclusions of this book up till this point.

Judging from the title of the book, "Spiritual Purification," I have written just about all I need to on this particular subject. However, I feel that I still need to touch on one very important point.

That is how do we get rid of or cancel out our karma. Unless you understand how to do that and actually do wipe out all traces of the karma that has been ruling your life, then you will never understand what true happiness is.

"Be exorcised and all your problems will be solved."

There are many people in the world who think like that. However, strictly speaking they could not be more wrong. True, if you undergo spiritual purification, spiritual impediments and some other problems will be resolved. But that hardly means that all problems in life will be swept away forever.

I touched on this point a little bit before, but let me return to it. Whenever a person is possessed by an evil spirit, there is a reason for it. Never, never does a person without reason and without warning become so possessed by an evil spirit.

Why should that be? First of all, we have the question of family legacy that we have already discussed in some detail. If the ancestors in a given family caused others to suffer in the past, then their descendants are going to have to pay the price of retribution for them. The karma surrounding such families – their family legacy so to speak – is a direct cause for members of the family becoming possessed by evil spirits.

However, we should not forget that there is another fundamental reason in addition to this family legacy. Each person also has his or her individual karma. In other words, each person brings karmic baggage with himself or herself from a previous existence.

If in a previous life that person had some problem related to carnal passion, then in this life too he or she will be born into a family consumed by lust or some other passion. You see this is a matter of atonement. There is a mutual interacting relationship here between individual karma and family karma.

In every case, a bewitching evil spirit shows up because of these straightforward factors: individual and family karma. They are the causes of all unhappiness and bad luck. And only by canceling out these two kinds of karma can you enjoy true happiness.

However, they cannot be done away with simply by exorcising them. Even if an evil spirit is cast out, the underlying cause of the possession – namely this two-headed karma – remains behind. No, I should not say that they cannot be done away with. But a single spiritual purification is not powerful enough to do the trick. In most cases, repeated spiritual purifications are required to eliminate the surface spiritual impediments. There still remain, however, spiritual impediments (in most cases derived from the ancestors) lurking deep down in the person's character and disposition. In order to root these out, the individual must change his or her entire person. And that takes time, of course. The only way to do it is to root out the defects of the old self naturally by relying on meritorious deeds, moral reform and spiritual enlightenment. As you get rid of the weight of karma, the span of years that you were allotted by Heaven at the time you were born can also be adjusted.

In other words, the length of your stay on earth, your character and your fate can all be improved by your efforts to conform to the Way of Heaven and follow its precepts as best you can. Think of it as being much like the process by which you are able by letting nature take its proper course to clear away the accumulated, petrified spiritual impediments that we have been talking about. The reason is that all of these things are related, and affect and reinforce each other.

However, what happens if by undergoing spiritual purification a person receives remission for all of his family and personal karma? For example, say he shows his sincerity of heart by making a *tamagushi* gift of ¥50,000, ¥100,000 or even ¥1,000,000. In return he is forgiven completely for all of his ancestors' sins as well as the burden of sin he brought with him into this world because of evil deeds committed in past lives. Such a trade-off might make you want to say, "The gods really are unfair."

If a donation of money can wipe out all these spiritual problems, the best philosophy of life would seem to be to do whatever the hell you like, pull out all the stops so to speak, and only when you see that you are nearing the end of the road hire somebody and tell him, "Please conduct a proper memorial service for me in exchange for this money."

Be advised however that the gods are not nearly as unfair or as unreasonable as you might surmise. Neither are they so forgiving. Heaven and nature are the same. All men stand equal before the court of karma – the fundamental law that governs the entire universe. In other words: good begets good; evil begets evil.

Consequently, the harvest of the seeds that you have sowed, you must reap in its entirety by yourself. Even if you undergo spiritual purification or take some similar step, you still will not be dealing with the fundamental problem of karma. Look upon spiritual purification as an important turning point that can leave you prepared to receive divine fortune. That is because it can extricate you from the family ties created by your karmic legacy, improve your character, change bad luck to good, and increase your good fortune. But the important thing is what you do with the days that follow.

What course of action then should you take? I explain the proper course for living in great detail in my book *Your Place in the Divine Order* and *Make Your Own Luck,* so I would ask you to refer to them. But here I would like to address the same problem from a slightly different angle.

Five Categories of Suffering

Basically there are two ways to get rid of the karmic legacy. The first is to accumulate enough merit to offset this spiritual debt. The second is to expiate your guilt through suffering. You might call the first method the positive method of karmic relief and the latter the negative method of karmic relief.

In other words, because karma really is nothing but the aggregate debt generated by the infliction of suffering and worry on others, in order to get rid of this debt you must either generate an equal amount of joy and happiness for others or you must suffer to the same degree that they have. It is like balancing the scales of justice. Naturally, however, troubles or suffering that come about through your lack of effort and diligence, or negligence cannot be considered as being karmic-related.

You might call them the simple result of extra-karmic natural law governing existence in this present life. In other words, you set yourself up for your own fall. You are receiving your just dessert. How then do you consciously go about getting rid of your karmic debt. Let's first look at the negative method of personal suffering.

We talk about "human suffering," but really it takes distinct forms in each particular case. Some people lack money. Some people have failed marriages. Other people are constantly ill. Or there are the students who simply cannot score good marks....Try to enumerate all the forms of unhappiness and you could go on forever. But in general I think you can divide the types of unhappiness into the following five categories.

1. Suffering related to death
2. Suffering related to poverty
3. Suffering related to illness
4. Suffering related to interacting with other people
5. Suffering related to employment (and marriage for women)

I like to refer to these as the "Five Categories of Suffering." If you carefully look at the many different kinds of suffering we encounter in life, you will find that whatever you are dealing with can inevitably be fitted neatly into one of these five categories.

Human beings taste one or more of these five kinds of suffering while they go about wiping out their personal and family karmic debts. However, most people do not understand the meaning of the whole process. People usually just think they suffer because they suffer.

"Why am I the only one who has to suffer?...."

"Why is it that my family alone has no luck?...."

They say such things over and over again to themselves, sighing all the while. Nothing could be more senseless. Despite the fact that they have been offered a golden chance to wipe out their karmic debt, such people are totally unconscious of and ungrateful for the opportunity. Instead, they end up clouding up their thinking even more than before. It is really quite understandable, but....

Let me offer a bit more detailed explanation of the real meaning of suffering.

Death: the Fastest Way to Eliminate Karmic Debt

Some families seem to suffer one death after the next. Almost as if they had been possessed by the god of death himself, such families lose their mainstay members or see newly born children die time after time – no sooner than they have come into the world.

I think many of my readers are familiar with the kind of family I am talking about. Without a doubt, members of such families undergo incredible suffering. A beloved spouse dies. A child – apple of his or her parents' eyes – is taken away without warning. Brothers and sisters disappear to the otherworld forever. When a loved one is lost, we have what is known as "the anguish of separation from loved ones." This is one of the most distressing trials of life referred to often in Buddhism. And few things can cause more pain in life.

How might you feel if you were the member of such a family that is constantly living with death?

"I wish he would go ahead and die."

"I don't mind being in this situation since I'll soon be in line for a nice inheritance." No doubt different people react in different ways. But the average person caught in such a situation is more likely to simply feel lost and weep with anguish.

He might say something like the following to himself: "I wouldn't care how much money it would cost; I'd pay for the very top medical treatment around if it would save father's life. Oh save him please."

Or: "Oh, dear gods, please forgive me for being so unfilial. In the future I promise to be the most filial child possible, if you'll only save my father's life."

These are the ways the average person would react to such a situation. Any person who would remain unmoved in the face of imminent death in his own family would have to be considered somehow abnormal.

Death in a family can cause such grief – grief unimaginable to the outsider. This is the kind of death that has no respect for money, status or reputation.

If you look at things another way, however, death is the most effective method for rapidly canceling out karmic debt. If the father in a family with such a long loss column on its ledger passes away quickly, then that means that the other members of the family do not have as far to go to atone for their past misdeeds. In some cases, the death of all the children in a family is the only way to ensure that descendants will not have to face the karmic mountain of retribution.

If members of a particular family keep dying off one after the next, then you can be sure that this family has a very grave karmic problem. That is because when the karmic ledger is too far out of kilter in the bad sense, Heaven sees death as the most appropriate positive method for bringing things back into equilibrium and eliminating the evil family legacy. Do not be mistaken on this point.

"Is that so?" you might respond. "Is death really the best remedy for a large family karmic debt? Well I don't know how long it's been since I started thinking, I want to die, I want to die.' So to hear you it would seem the best possible thing I could do for the world, for other people, for our ancestors, and even for our descendants, would be to abandon hope and in all sincerity commit suicide. No, better yet, our whole immediate family should go together. That would do even more to settle the karmic debt, wouldn't it?"

The fact is that individual or family suicides *(shinju)*, although in a sense an expression of supreme effort and devotion, do not balance the suffering caused as a result and accomplish absolutely nothing as far as getting rid of bad karma is concerned. On the contrary, because people who commit suicide have not developed their divinely given talents and lived the span of life that Heaven had ordained, they commit the sin of *amatsutsumi* – defiance of Heaven. The spirits of those who have committed suicide fall into a special hell. There everything more than one-meter away from them is pitch black. The worst part is that the suffering they experienced at the moment of death continues for all eternity.

Speaking in terms of the divine laws, the sins of avoidance or spiritual laziness are abhorred three times as much as are sins of excess, such as egotism, conceit and overbearingness. The reason that should be is that if the arrogant individual reflects on his mistakes and mends his ways, the benefit of his experiences and knowledge still remains. On the other hand, with the perpetrator of sins of neglect, there is nothing to be left behind in his soul no matter how much he might reflect on his errors.

So the expiation through death that I am referring to here involves things that are out of the hands of human beings, such as unavoidable accidents or illnesses that do not yield to any amount of treatment or care. I am talking about the 19-year-old oldest son who unexpectedly dies. I am talking about the oldest daughter who is born sickly and finally succumbs at age seven. Let me reiterate that you should not have any misunderstandings in this regard.

Trouble With Money Is a Form of Atonement

After death, the biggest source of suffering is money.

Lives of abject poverty. Lives full of fear of bill collectors. The world is overflowing with people who face serious money problems. Every day they suffer to a degree comparable with death itself. Many wish they could only enjoy the luxury of death; that at least would be a release from their earthly suffering.

Honestly, it is not at all unusual for people suffering in this manner ultimately to choose the path of suicide. In the worst instances, they take their entire family – little children included – on the dark, eternal journey.

Looking at such behavior no one can seriously doubt that money woes can torture the soul. But why exactly are people so bothered by money worries? It is of course because of their karmic connections. If you are being driven mad by money problems, I would say that they are probably due to the fact that an ancestor of yours used money to hurt others or was consumed with covetousness, or maybe in one of your past lives you did to others what is now being done to you. For any of these reasons, or similar reasons, you are having to atone in this life.

But take heart because by undergoing this suffering now you are helping to wipe out the karmic debt of yourself and your ancestors.

As with the case of death, for many people, suffering from money problems is far more effective as a means of ridding themselves of karmic debt than the most strenuous efforts they might make on their own. For example, some wives are forced to shoulder the debts of their husbands. Or a beloved child has an incurable disease that costs huge amounts of money to treat. Such people have to pay and pay all their lives through.

Illness Is Another Way to Pay Off Karmic Debts

The third important method for paying off karmic debt is through the suffering involved in illness.

People who are born without the full use of their limbs or congenital diseases. People who spend much of their lifetime fighting a serious illness. People who always have something wrong with themselves in some portion of their bodies... The suffering that these people endure is a tool to wipe out their karmic legacy. However, this explanation does not apply when the problem is caused by an individual's abuse of his or her own body.

Colds, broken bones and other transitory medical problems really do not cause all that much suffering. But should a person contract an incurable disease, then the individual himself and all the members of his family will share a living hell on earth. Sometimes that suffering will become so bad that the person will even choose to take his own life.

Consequently, the suffering caused by such illnesses, depending on the degree, can in many cases be just as serious as that related to problems with money. In other words, if the sickness is comparatively minor, then it will not match in intensity the suffering caused by money woes. But if the disease is serious, then it can be worse than the quagmire caused by money problems.

In any event, death, money and illness rank tops in that order when it comes to causing suffering related to karmic debt. On the other hand, they are the best three methods for quickly eliminating that same debt.

Complicated Human Relations

The fourth method for reducing the karmic debit column is through the suffering caused by complicated human relationships.

The opposite of the three conditions I just described would be a long life, plenty of money and a healthy body. A person who enjoys all three might be said to be living tolerably well.

However, even those three conditions do not guarantee a truly happy life.

For example if a worker is constantly being harassed by his boss, can he claim to be happy? What about the man who ended up with a real shrew for a wife? Or what about the wife who is shackled to a real bastard, who beats her, kicks her and cheats on her constantly – a monster whom she can respect neither as a man nor as a human being. People caught in such situations can hardly be said to be happy. When human relations are severely strained, people suffer and become exasperated with worry.

This conflict between individuals usually becomes most severe among married couples. A woman is married to a lazy good-for-nothing, who spends all of his time boozed up. She finally leaves him and gets remarried only to find that her new husband is even worse. Or a man has a wife who not only runs around on him but leaves him to come home to dark rooms and cold pots....Such marital situations are far from few. And the misery involved is unimaginable to the bystander.

Just look at the many instances in which people who have unhappy family or marital relationships are driven to suicide and this should all be clear to you. Sometimes even though a man is in the best of health and has no money worries, he will take his precious life because of problems with his wife, mother-in-law, sister-in-law or whomever. The same holds true for his wife. The suffering that results from complications in human relations can be truly awful.

Eliminating Bad Karma Affecting Employment

To enjoy a long life, be blessed with good health and financial security, while also enjoying good human relations. That would probably constitute a good definition of happiness for most people.

But even some people who have all these things sometimes still suffer when the job they are doing is not appropriate for them. We might say that they suffer because they cannot develop their capabilities, talents and dreams the way they want to. For most women marriage is the center of their life – a lifelong career you might call it – so they are naturally concerned to make a suitable match. Too often though, women end up with mates who leave something to be desired.

These men might treat their wives all right, but somehow their tastes do not really match those of their spouses, and they refuse to accept responsibility for helping make their wives more complete human beings, who can develop their own potential while contributing fully to their families and society. As a result, although the relationships in such marriages are comparatively not really all that bad, the wives are unable to express themselves fully. They end up being what I like to call "hired wives." And their luck is to be stuck in a dead-end job. And as I have said, such a situation does not represent a truly happy life.

Now to get back to the discussion of poor luck with jobs. Obviously there are situations in which a man is not particularly suited to the job, hates the business he is in, or in any event does not put out sufficiently to succeed. It is the individual himself who is to blame in such cases. But these situations are separate from what I am discussing. No, I am talking about the kind of fellow who tries and tries but still always ends up having to engage in work that he detests. Such cases are attributable to poor karma.

"I have things that I would rather do, but because I have been forced into carrying on the family business, every day I have to keep doing the same job – a job that I really hate."

In cases like this, the thing to do is to think that it is the process of getting rid of the poor karma that is making the person's life miserable.

However, it should be remembered that suffering like this caused by job problems is really the least important kind of spiritual complication. There is no denying that people involved in such situations are a lot better off than are those who are suffering by reason of death, serious illness or friction in human relationships. In general, what these people, who are morning in and morning out worrying about their woes, need to do is step back and consider where they are on the five-tier scale of karmic suffering. They will then realize that others are suffering far more than them. In other words, they are suffering comparatively little. By totally accepting that reality and understanding how comparatively good their fate is, they will develop feelings of gratitude for their lot.

It is frequently said that satori or enlightenment really is the acceptance without reservation of one's own karma. But such people go around complaining about how cruel fate has been to them. Such an attitude hardly reflects enlightenment about anything. I firmly believe that the truly enlightened person is the one who admits frankly that his personal karma is really not all that bad, and is filled with gratitude to his ancestors and the gods in this regard. As a result, he consciously seeks to live life in a bright, healthy manner. This is what real enlightenment is all about.

The Spirit May Be Gone, but Not the Karma

As I noted earlier, the quickest way to wipe out bad karma is through death. The family head dies while still young. Small children in the family die one after the next. These are the ways in which the gods wipe out the evil karma in the quickest fashion possible. And as I mentioned earlier, you can be sure that a family that suffers early or frequent deaths has a complicated karmic legacy.

The divine world makes sure that a soul which has a heavy karmic penalty to work off is born into such a family. The divine message is: "This is a house that owes an early death. This is where you were meant to be. This is your home..." And so the person is reborn into such a suitable family. This is the principle of suitability at work.

Families that tend to suffer early deaths generation after generation are in the grip of a common fate, which when it manifests itself openly does so in the form of spiritual impediments and ill luck.

For example, the spirits of people killed by such a family's ancestors will always be lurking around looking for an opportunity to exact revenge; and such revenge is often realized in the form of early death among the descendants of the "enemy."

For that reason, when I carry out a spiritual purification on a person belonging to such an ill-fated family, problems of early death or debilitating illness often clear up. Don't be fooled, however. Even if I or another master of spiritual purification manages to expel the vengeful spirit, in cases where the fundamental problem is the family karma itself, we may get rid of the interference from the spirit world, but the bad karma will tend to resurface in the form of atrocious luck.

In other words, the spiritual purification will get rid of the mischievous spirit, but it will leave the family karma behind. Naturally, however, if the person who has been exorcised made a small *tamagushi* offering with the greatest of sincerity, and offered thanks with complete self-awareness after suitable reflection, the gods will recognize the merit of these actions and reduce the karmic weight on the family. It is for that reason that spiritual purification represents a great opportunity for many people – in fact it can be a fundamental turning point in their lives.

How then should we confront karma and its aftereffects in ourselves and our families?

Acquire Merit Even While Suffering

Through the five kinds of suffering I have described – related to death, poverty, illness, human relations and employment – we gradually reduce the deficit in our karmic account. However, there is another way in which we can do the same thing.

I am referring of course to the accumulation of merit – something I touched on earlier. People born with a complicated karmic legacy can through various acts of service sustained over a long period of time accumulate merit that helps to reduce little bit by little bit their karmic load. In effect, this is a method for offsetting the debits in the karmic account.

Some of my readers no doubt are thinking: "Well that's just jim dandy. I never was much into suffering anyway. I'll just start doing good deeds to get rid of my bad karma."

But such thinking is nothing more than wishful thinking.

As long as any of the karmic debt remains, there is no escape from suffering. No matter how hard you might try to accumulate merit, as long as bad personal karma survives, you are going to have to suffer in one form or another. But while in no way violating this fundamental principle of karma, accumulation of merit can do much good. This is how it works:

In response to good deeds, the gods and Buddha offer their protection and Heaven also moves to do its part. These are manifested in the form of compassion that decreases great and small difficulties alike. Their grace and compassion allow difficulties originally scheduled for a person's old age to be moved up to his youth. The person who has been accumulating merit also receives divine assistance in the form of endurance, vigor, grit and spiritual strength. These divine gifts enable the person to overcome difficulties, develop and achieve success, while also affording him the opportunity to meet good teachers and friends.

So, we might conclude that the most effective method for eliminating bad karma is through simultaneous accumulation of merit while undergoing suffering.

To put it a different way, suffering does not remain mere suffering. It is transformed into a type of suffering that accumulates merit. If we welcome the inevitable suffering, it acts as a kind of "detonator" and also further increases merit. This process, including the continuous accumulation of merit, results in the development of a strong spirit that is defiant before bad karma. The person who possesses such an indomitable spirit is not afraid of suffering. Rather he flings himself into the fires of suffering. This is a very good strategy because what happens is that the passions of the heart are eventually extinguished and the fires of the soul cooled.

This forward-looking strategy also causes the person to forget his suffering. Once we are born, there is no way we can escape from the suffering attendant to life. Run here or there as we might, we are still going to encounter our destined share of pain, bitterness and worries and there are certain to be days when the tears roll down our faces. If that is the way it is, then we should throw ourselves fearlessly into the business of living.

Just remember. No matter how complicated your family's karmic legacy may be and no matter how much you may be plagued by your own karma, every fleeting second on earth is infinitely preferable to a sojourn in hell. Life on earth is truly a wonderful thing that should be treasured. Our bodies may suffer at times, but those condemned to hundreds of years in hell view us with incredible envy. We are stuck with this shell of flesh, that is true, but even as we work off our karma through suffering, we are in a much better position than those poor souls in hell.

Furthermore, those of us born in modern Japan are truly blessed when it comes to clothing, food and a place to live, not to mention personal freedom. Just think what life would be like if you were born at the bottom of the social ladder in a country like India or Bangladesh. Or what would you do if you were born the son of a Palestinian guerrilla? Lives such as those are little different from the situation of the souls in hell. If you consider that fact, you can see how lucky we really are. Even if we speak of suffering, everything is relative. And we are relatively lucky. Just think, even if we have to suffer at times, we were born into a country and in an age where we have the opportunity to accumulate merit.

Gaining Merit Through Spiritual Purification

However, as the old saying goes: "To talk is easy; to act is difficult." That sums up how easy it is for human beings to deceive themselves. In too many cases, although we are determined to develop our own character and to give our all for the sake of our fellow human beings, we end up falling victim to the temptations of procrastination and laziness and never do strive to accumulate merit as we should.

Probably some of my readers know exactly what I am referring to here. The reason is that persons so inclined find themselves unable to acquire the initial virtue required to set the ball in motion – to start the process of accumulating merit. And the reason why that personal virtue should remain hidden is none other than interference from the spirit world. Precisely because of these spiritual obstacles, no matter how much the person wants to accumulate merit or wants to exert himself in a spiritual sense, because of the interference from evil spirits, nothing of real value is ever achieved.

Even if such a person summons up what he thinks is his entire will to move forward positively, something inevitably happens to derail his plans. He is struck down by illness or has family troubles.

The upshot is that everything ends up falling apart. The only way out of this situation is through the power of increased resolve and strength of character.

In any event, the average person who desires to positively work to accumulate merit first needs to eliminate this interference from the spirit world. And the way to do that of course is through spiritual purification.

If a spiritual purification is performed, then illness and other visible problems created by the spirits often completely disappear. Even if they do not disappear just like that, they will go away little bit by little bit. I suppose it is unavoidable that with that said some people are going to consider a spiritual purification as simply a method for curing disease. But nothing could be further from the truth.

A spiritual purification will not necessarily help improve a person's fortune in every aspect of life. It might be able to restore a person to tip-top physical condition. But that does not mean that it can make a rather dense city councilman become prime minister, or catapult the beer company with the smallest market share in three months to the top of the industry. Heaven's blessings do not operate like that, but unfortunately many people who turn to the gods and the spirit world for help are looking for results that are equally fantastic.

For example, sometimes psychics like myself get a joker who comes along and says something like this to us, "I gave ¥30 million in alms, so won't you help increase my crop production by putting a second sun up there in the sky. I understand that you claim to receive messages directly from the all-knowing, all-powerful god of the universe through your telepathic powers, so it shouldn't be any problem for you. They say you can immediately heal any disease around. So making another sun should be a snap for you."

When a person with a little spiritual or psychic power becomes too arrogant in the way he treats others, he is likely to run into somebody like this.

Even the greatest of spiritual leaders, say Moses or Onisaburo Deguchi, men who were able to part the seas or cause huge meteorites to roll up slope, were incapable of adding five or six moons above, making Venus elongate or changing the Earth's shape to a parallelogram. These are things that only the supreme god who created the universe can do. As you can see, even human beings endowed with outstanding spiritual or psychic powers are not very powerful in the overall scheme of things.

For these reasons it is important for us to study with the greatest of humility the laws of Heaven and the laws of nature and together render due respect to our Maker. If we do diligently and righteously follow the Way, the sincerity that makes us strive to do better will always remain intact.

Accordingly, in order to become a true spiritualist or clairvoyant, a person must first recognize deep in his soul that the spiritual or psychic powers that he possesses are but an infinitesimal fraction of the power of the gods. He must understand that he needs to sincerely follow the Way of Heaven and never become too dependent on the powers he has been endowed with. Nor should he become arrogant about them or flaunt them.

Instead, those few people endowed with extraordinary powers should always employ them for good. They will then be treasured by both the gods and their fellow men, because they are doing their utmost to perform good deeds here on earth and make the world a better place. This more than anything is the message that the creator of the universe, the all-knowing, all-powerful divinity that controls all, wants to get across to those lucky few of us who have been blessed by Heaven with special spiritual powers.

Well, you must excuse me for again going off on a tangent. Let us return to our discussion of spiritual purification. Through spiritual purification the spirit becomes cleansed. As I described earlier, karmic residue still remains behind. But even so, once the physical disease that has afflicted them has been cured, many people can achieve a complete turnaround in their lives. The reason for that is that they now have open to them broad new chances to achieve merit and to begin to change their luck. To be more precise, they have created the various conditions needed to change their fortunes.

Even though prior to the spiritual purification that person might have really wanted deep in his heart to be useful to others, he was unable to do so because of problems on the job or in his relations with other people. Now, however, he suddenly finds that with the interference from the spirit world brought to a halt, he has all kinds of unforeseen opportunities to contribute to society.

And thanks to this new, wide vista of opportunities, his luck also begins to change. It is just like a situation where dark clouds clear away and the bright sun comes shining through. Only in this case the soul brightens and the entrance to the path that will enable that individual to begin erasing the karmic legacy of his family and his own past lives stands beckoning before him.

Well then, as you can see, it is simply not sufficient to want to work for the sake of the world and humankind. In order to realize this desire, you first have to use the golden opportunity afforded by your spiritual purification to create the environment in which you can do your best for this cause. But thanks to the spiritual purification your chances to change bad luck to strong and divine fortune will increase tremendously.

The More Reincarnations, the More Talent

How many times have the people on earth today been reincarnated? That is a very interesting question.

When I do an expert analysis of a person's past spiritual history I go back, far back in time. Experience in this area would lead me to believe that everyone around today first came into existence around 158,000 years ago.

At that time many of the people living in Japan had the title *mikoto*, or "prince," attached to their names. It was the "age of the gods." In those days long ago, it also seems probable that the culturally sophisticated continent of Mu was in existence and human beings were quite familiar with both the invisible world of the gods and our phenomenal world. You might think of it as an age in which gods and human beings lived on the same plane.

If you are talking about the "deepest soul," then the process of regeneration and therefore human history can be said to extend back some 600 million years. But if we are only referring to the youngest or *mototsu* soul, then the process of human reincarnation began from the age that we are discussing here.

Consequently, the average person alive today has already been reborn some 47 to 50 times. Of course, there are some individuals who have been born 70 times, or even 100 times. But people born 100 times or more account for only about one out of every 50 of the residents of cities in civilized countries. In modern times rebirths have tended to occur about once every 300 years, but in ancient times the pace of the process was much more leisurely.

What then happens to human beings during rebirths? They are busy storing up talents and virtues. What exactly do we mean by talents? Well, as I explain in detail in *Your Place in the Divine*

Order, they are accomplishments related to knowledge, the arts and faith.

Some people are born intelligent, others have a highly developed aesthetic sense and still others are seemingly brimming over with faith. The reason in each case is that they made great progress in these areas in their past lives.

In addition, generally speaking the more reincarnations a person has undergone, the more talents he or she has acquired. The degree to which this has happened is especially evident in a person's voice. Regardless of whether the voice is high- or low-pitched, a person with a beautiful resonant voice no doubt has been through many, many reincarnations.

But this is only generally true. Some people have only been reincarnated a few times, but they have taken advantage of each and every rebirth and stay on earth to the utmost, thereby developing their talents. On the other hand, there are those souls that go through one rebirth after the other but always seem to do things in slapdash fashion. As a result, they make very little spiritual progress.

So, as you can see, a large number of rebirths in and of itself does not guarantee a great deal of talent. But the general pattern is: the greater the number of rebirths, the greater the amount of talent a person possesses.

You often hear people saying things like: "That fellow's really talented, but he never seems to be able to make his mark in the world." And it is true, there are a lot of people in this world who are blessed with talent that never seems to bring them any luck. But why should their luck be so bad? To put it simply: they lack virtue.

In order to actually become a success in the real world, a person must have ability and initiative. But another essential condition is that he have virtue.

210

For example, some people who lack talent but possess virtue amaze the world with their success. You look at a work by a painter who is obviously short on technical talent, and yet it somehow strangely grabs you. It creates a certain kind of special mood or perhaps it possesses some other indescribable characteristic. So you end up praising the work in spite of yourself. No doubt you can think of many singers or media personalities who do not have much native ability but still have captured the public's attention.

The three things most valuable to people are drive, talent and virtue. Individuals in which these three capabilities are most developed tend to have been reincarnated many times. And each time they returned to earth they did their best for the individuals they encountered and society in general. For that reason, into their souls have been incised latent memories of their past lives, subconscious thinking and a deep moral sense.

Why Ancestors Torment Their Descendants

Well, again I have digressed a bit. Let's return to the question of family and personal karma and their residual effects.

As I explained, human beings are born into families that are appropriate for them in terms of their own karmic balance sheet. After that happens, an individual has to deal with both his personal karmic legacy and the troubles of the family in question. This all adds up to suffering when the two types of karma are bad. For example, he may be possessed by a vengeful spirit that has been shadowing the family for generations or by an ancestor who has been sent to hell. One way or another he will have to pay off the karmic debt from earlier lives.

I think most of my readers probably understand this basic

situation now. But probably some of you have some doubts, such as reflected in the following statement.

"I can see where a vengeful spirit might take on its wrath on the descendants. But I can't comprehend why an ancestor who has been condemned to hell would possess his own descendants and cause them grief. If he was any kind of real ancestor at all, it would seem natural that he would desire to protect those very descendants. It wouldn't seem to make any sense for him to possess and torment his descendants just because he himself is suffering terribly. I simply can't understand what's happening in such cases."

Everything that this person has said is absolutely true.

It is for that very reason that I sometimes have to lecture these ancestral spirits. I tell them something like the following:

"You spirits think of no one but yourselves. All of your present suffering is due to your own wicked deeds. There is no way you can relieve your own suffering by possessing your descendants. To think so is sheer lunacy. Leave them alone and attend to the business of rectifying your own souls while praying to the gods and Buddha for their protection. That is how you should be carrying out your spiritual rehabilitation. No matter how awful the suffering you may experience in any hell, if you sincerely pray, then the gods and Buddha will shine on you their saving light and ease your suffering."

But no matter how much I lecture them, these ancestral spirits stuck in hell stubbornly refuse to mend their ways. This despite the fact that if they would have a change of heart, then they would probably be in absolutely no danger of falling deeper into hell.

But let me explain why it is that these ancestral spirits take possession of the souls of their descendants. As I pointed out earlier, the process by which a living person wipes out his karmic debt is linked to the process by which his ancestors reform their souls. Now I would like to look at the drama of how an individual changes his spiritual outlook and reforms himself, as seen through the filter of the perspective of the spiritual world.

One reason why all of this happens the way that it does is that by suffering at the same time that his ancestors are suffering a person can pay off some of the debt of past lives – a kind of atonement through suffering.

Another reason is that in accordance with a divine plan, the painful experiences resulting from being possessed sear themselves into the soul of the person who is so possessed. The resulting lessons learned, travails and sadness together serve as a kind of fertilizer for his or her destined future mission on this earth. In other words, the individual is steeled in the fiery furnace of suffering and comes out a better person because of this difficult metamorphosis. The gods arrange for all this to happen so that when the process has been completed the person will be able to make great contributions to society. It is Heaven's way of testing souls, if you will.

The third reason why ancestors choose to possess their own descendants is their realization that by having all of them suffer together, they can help wipe clean the family's karmic slate.

This is very typical of the way the gods do things. They like to kill three birds with one stone, so to speak. Keep this fact in mind as I explain the interrelation between blood and ancestors.

Here I am not simply talking about blood types: A, B, O or whatever. The fact is that the special characteristics of a family are transmitted down through the ages through the blood. I am indebted to my own spiritual mentor Aiko Uematsu for this particular bit of information.

(What follows is a telepathy conversation with Mrs Uematsu.)

Uematsu: In a sense, all of us are sent to earth as representatives of our ancestors. It's like we are carrying their memorial tablets on our backs. On top of that, within our blood is contained a record of all that our ancestors did – the good and the bad. Lurking within it as well are our talents and character traits. Consequently, when during our daily lives we have good thoughts or we pay attention to the good vibrations sent out by the gods, our blood is purified naturally and the good blood passed down from our ancestors is reinvigorated. As a result, our talents and good personality traits bloom. Life can be described as the will and thoughts of our ancestors and the gods as they have been infused into us through the medium of our blood.

In Japanese the word for blood is *chi*. A homonym means wisdom or knowledge. That is very appropriate, since much of the wisdom that comes to us emerges from our bloodstream. In the final analysis, the knowledge that really counts, what we need to manage our daily lives successfully, is not something that you can acquire on your own no matter how many books you read or how many people you talk to. It is something that wells up out of the blood that streams through your body as you move about. For that reason you need to be conscious of your body and to express yourself through body language. Should you fail to do so, then no matter how fine your brain may be, you will be one of those people who is worthless when it comes to achieving anything practical in daily life. How much is a university education really worth in daily life? If we want to receive true wisdom we need to look to our bodies for it. Remember the role of the body, Mr. Fukami....Mr. Fukami. Fukami. Are you listening to me?

Fukami: Ah....ah, certainly. I'm listening....I'm listening. That reminds me of a good joke about food poisoning.

Uematsu: This is no laughing matter.

Fukami: Our three-dimensional world is known as the *jigenkai* and *ji* is also a homonym for "hemorrhoids." So I guess if you sit in one place too long you are sure to enter the *jigenkai*.

Uematsu: Keep making uncouth jokes like that and you'll get the gods angry at you.

Fukami: Angry at me....

Uematsu: I hope you're not going to continue with this.

Fukami: Since you're my teacher, you shouldn't be at a loss for a reply.

Uematsu: Let's stop all this foolishness and get back to the discussion of wisdom.

Fukami: Well, at present I am undergoing training to facilitate the emergence of wisdom from my bloodstream.

Uematsu: I think you're just getting ready to make another corny joke.

Fukami: I'm studying *waka* poetry and paying special attention to homonyms.

Uematsu: Hmm.

Fukami: Today I finally realized why it is that most people, even when they are middle-aged and chubby, have relatively straight backs.

Uematsu: How is that?

Fukami: It's because as the proxy of their ancestors they have to carry their ancestral tablets on their backs.

Uematsu: Well, you just went and made another sick pun in your explanation. Let me warn you that if you keep spouting off like that you're going to make a farce out of a serious book like this.

Fukami: I agree entirely. From when I first put pen to paper, I took the whole thing very seriously and tried to write something of value. I worked at a breakneck pace to do it, too. In any event, considering the content...Well, what I'm trying to say is page after page we've been looking at things like the karmic legacy left by ancestors, suffering in hell, interference from the spirit world...things like that. Everything so dark, weighty and with explanations couched in difficult terminology. I thought my readers might have become a little bit exhausted reading all these things. So that is why I wanted to talk with you Mrs. Uematsu – to bring some of your quick wit and cheerfulness to bear.

Uematsu: I must admit this book is a bit on the ponderous side. I think you are at your best when you are as you are in your seminars: bright, interesting, but focused and serious when you need to be.

Fukami: I'd have to agree with that assessment, Mrs. Uematsu. I too like doing things that way best, and it's easiest too. Don't worry, I'll make my next book as cheerful as can be. But after this little respite of ours I have to return to a heavy topic – a detailed discussion of the fate of unborn children. That is certainly a dark, weighty subject, but there are many things related to it that my readers need to know on the subject. I know that some of my readers are people who have no real problems to speak of. And as they got deeper and deeper into the heavy content of the book, they must have felt those contents somewhat oppressive. I realized that while I was writing it. The thing is, I want to help those people who have been deluded by evil spirits, those people who do not know what is true anymore, those people who find their karmic legacy too much to bear, those people who cannot escape from countless worries. I want these spirits who died with a heavy karmic load or numerous troubles and who now might be possessing readers of this book while yearning for release from their suffering to understand my message. And I wish to exorcise the souls of such readers while bringing release to the tormented spirits through the process of spiritual purification.

Now, let's return to the normal world.

As Mrs. Uematsu explained, inside our blood is to be found all the legacy of our ancestors – the essence of our being. As for where the power of this blood emanates from: it is the area of the spine. I verified this fact with my own eyes when the gods granted me the power of divine vision. With some people, from near the first or second cervical vertebrae in the zone stretching from the vicinity of the coccyx or sacral bone you will find something resembling black sesame seeds ranged tightly in a vertical line. "What on earth are these things?" I thought to myself as I stared at them for the first time. Then gradually they began to expand, growing bigger and bigger. Then when I looked very closely I could see that they were tiny men in ceremonial dress, some dressed as Shinto priests, some in the robes of Buddhist priests, others in layers of kimono. This band of ancestral spirits included jubilant faces and anguished faces. They looked just like a line of ants.

Then it suddenly dawned on me for the first time what we had here was a collection of ancestral spirits all crammed in together near the vertebrae. It was just as Mrs. Uematsu had instructed me. It was as if the vertebrae were memorial tablets inscribed with the names of ancestors of a person's family and that individual was carrying them around on his back all the time.

Mrs. Uematsu had indeed been right. However, this is not something that is normally revealed. This condition is in effect a kind of link between living descendants and their ancestors – a bridge between the here and now and the spirit world. Nevertheless, knowledge of what is really happening allows us to understand why the disease known as caries of the vertebrae really comes about. It is because of a strong spiritual intervention on the part of ancestors to cause suffering such as we discussed earlier.

Abortion Displeases Heaven

Finally, I would like to discuss in some detail the question of unborn babies.

I touched briefly on the problem of aborted babies in Chapter 1 and made a detailed analysis of it in *Divine Powers*. If you read those sections, I think you will get a very clear idea about what I am talking about. But the fact is that questions in regard to aborted babies continue to stream in all the time. So I will again here discuss the issue in some detail.

But first, I must make another point. That is that spirits of unborn babies have a definite existence of their own.

In today's world there are a good number of people who are absolutely convinced that there is no such thing as the spirit of an unborn baby. But they are very wrong.

It is impossible to show physical evidence of this fact. But if you use psychic methods, you can actually verify the existence of these spirits.

Usually two and a half or three months into a pregnancy, the fetus already has a spirit, endowed with a degree of consciousness. In most cases, by eight or nine months it develops a real soul, including the *kushimitama* – the most important part of our personal spiritual make-up. Now should a miscarriage or abortion take place anytime between when the spirit first enters the fetus and the predetermined time of natural child birth, the spirit of the child will be left behind – a spirit that bears a grudge against this world.

Actually, even though the physical result is the same, a miscarriage and artificial abortion are two completely different things. With a miscarriage the child's spirit remains; that is true. But that unfortunate result is certainly not looked upon by the gods as a sin.

The problem lies with artificial abortion.

Abortion is the prevention of the birth of a baby that if left unbothered would be born naturally. It therefore amounts to a form of murder and in the eyes of the gods is a crime. Even if that is not true under the law of man it is true under the law of Heaven. But I hasten to add that it is not one of the more serious crimes.

The reason why it is a crime is that the mother's ability to give birth was a gift from Heaven and nature. Many women who have abortions defend themselves by saying, "I'm the one who is giving birth, so it is my baby, my decision."

Of course, such a feeling is understandable. But if you consider the situation carefully, it becomes clear that such thinking is misguided. The ability to give birth is as I have said a gift from Heaven and nature. Put another way, that means it comes from the gods, specifically the creator of the universe. That is the reason for the saying, "A newborn is a gift from Heaven."

Defiance of the will of Heaven and artificial murder of the fetus is a sin in the eyes of the gods.

For that reason people who have aborted a child are punished after they die, albeit not in too severe a fashion.

Gloomy Womb Spirits

Next I would like to address the question of what spiritual repercussions an abortion has.

To put it in a nutshell, after an abortion the spirit of the womb is very gloomy. The spirit is to be found in the vicinity of the womb at the spot where it is in contact with the spirit world. If a woman has an abortion, this spirit clouds over – becomes blurry. If you view one through psychic eyes, you can see that in the case where one child has been aborted, the spirit is beige. If the woman has aborted two children, the second is a deep beige. The color gets darker as the number of abortions increases. The third and fourth are an olive brown or light black. This color phenomenon is the first spiritual effect of an abortion.

I conduct spiritual purification of the spirits of aborted babies. The procedure is to first ask the forgiveness of the gods for the murder of the child. Next, I have to conduct a purification rite to remove the cloudiness, the gloom, the contamination. The goal is to get the color to return to a white, crystalline kind of purity.

Incidentally, an abortion is not the only time when a womb can become cloudy and gloomy. It also happens when the pregnant woman engages in sex with warped motives.

When a couple who are truly in love have sex, the womb shines. But if money or some other ulterior motive is involved, it becomes black.

On the other hand, if a woman has sex with pure motives, the act is always beautiful even if the woman has had relations with many men before. In other words, the number of times that she has engaged in the act is totally irrelevant; it is her emotions at any particular time that the divine world is concerned with. If her motives are pure, then it does not matter whether her conduct conforms to the dictums of traditional morality.

I am sure some of you would now like to ask the question, "Does that mean that if her motive is pure a woman can have sex with as many men as she wants as often as she wants?"

Well, the truth is that if the man and woman are both virgins when they engage in the act of sex that conceives a child, a child with the most pure soul possible will be born to them as a result. That is the truth. Now an adult woman may change partners and be absolutely pure in intentions with the man she is involved with at that particular time. But the fact is that she is hiding her past in the crevices of her heart, afraid that if she told her partner about it he would hate her. She therefore always is silently calculating. And under such circumstances the degree of purity in her heart is certain to decrease.

Just because a person is convinced that his or her love is honest does not mean that we can call it pure. It just means that on each occasion that person gives his or her all in the love relationship.

But what we have to remember here is that no matter how much a couple with less than pure backgrounds wants to bestow a pure soul on their offspring, there are limits to how pure that soul can really be. The offspring of a frog can be nothing but a frog. However, let me hasten to add that a woman who originally had a very beautiful soul, but who lost a little bit of that purity later in life still should be able to give birth to a child that will have a soul as beautiful as it would have been in the first place.

But what happens when a child conceived from a womb that had been cloudy from the start is brought into the world? What kind of child will this baby that does not measure very high on the purity index turn out to be? Most likely it will be a rebellious kid with a warped personality.

As the saying "The newborn is a gift from Heaven" makes clear, the soul that is in the child when it is born has come down from the spirit world. But that soul is made to match the character and quality and purity of the womb spirit. Consequently, in cases where the womb spirit is clouded over, as I mentioned earlier you are likely to end up with a problem child.

Conversely, if the womb spirit is pure and crystal clear in color, then a beautiful soul will lodge in the child. By a child with a beautiful soul, I mean a person who is honest by nature and who looks at things in a straightforward manner and grows up the way nature intended him to. On the other hand, a child with a poor soul will as I mentioned earlier have exactly the opposite kind of personality. The first type of child will win the deep love of his parents and make himself endeared to all he meets. And of course the guardian gods and spirits will keep an affectionate eye out for his welfare. Nothing pleases these guardian gods and spirits more than a gentle, honest child. As a result, children who are born with crystal-clear fetal spirits are rewarded with good fortune in life by the divine and spirit worlds.

The case is quite different for children with cloudy, gloomy spirits. The cloudier the womb spirit, the cloudier will be the soul of the child. What you end up getting are children with perverted souls and numerous character defects, who are stubborn and strong-willed, destructively rebellious and who are always attracted to the negative side of things.

"The older brother is such a good boy, why should it be that his younger brother is so rebellious?"

Often you will hear mothers moaning their fate in such a fashion. The fact is that the spiritual state of the child reflects the inner world of the mother and father at the time of his or her conception. Heaven fashions the soul of a child in accordance with the environment and feelings existing at that time in order to reflect the psychology and inner feelings of the parents at that moment.

That same situation holds true for a woman who has had several abortions. Of course, whether a child turns out to be good or bad and is obedient and honest or not does not depend solely on the state of the womb spirit at the time of birth. That is because the child's education after birth is an even more important factor. Suffice it to say that if the soul of the child and its womb spirit have been good, after the child has been born his or her education should be a relatively easy task. Conversely, children associated with cloudy womb spirits who have damaged souls are going to cause their parents a lot of trouble during their education. In the end, all of this hassle might be viewed as atonement for the sins of the parents.

Consequently, when a spiritual purification for an aborted baby is carried out, the first thing that needs to be done is to pray to the gods for forgiveness, so that the cloudiness and impurity of the womb spirit can be made clean.

Twin Feelings of the Aborted Babies

The second possible effect of an abortion is spiritual interference affecting the parents or brothers and sisters of the unborn child. But it must be admitted that the spiritual interference from aborted babies is really not all that strong to begin with.

Previously I encountered a woman who told me, "I am absolutely convinced that my husband, who was 56 when he died, was killed by the spirit of our aborted babies." She admitted that she had had two abortions, so that is why she came to that conclusion. I had to set her straight, however. Such a thing is totally impossible. The spirits of aborted babies do not have the spiritual power to threaten anyone's life.

There are a number of parapsychics around who are spreading the notion that the spirit of an aborted baby can seek its revenge in the form of a life-threatening illness. Nothing could be farther from the truth. Let me emphasize that you should not allow yourself to be deceived in this connection.

The spiritual interference that the spirits of aborted babies can cause amounts to minor influence on the mind and body of the mother and those youngsters who would have been their siblings. That is all they are capable of. Before I get into the details in that regard, I would first like to describe the feelings of these aborted children. In general, the spirits of aborted babies are obsessed with two different feelings. First, they hold a grudge against their parents. "Why did you conceive me and then just kill me to suit your own convenience," they think to themselves. Second, they are also jealous of their brothers and sisters.

"Look how much my brothers are fawned over, while I am abandoned and forgotten and so alone all the time. Oh, I wish I were older brother. How I envy younger brother." They express their jealousy in such terms.

So they are entrapped in these two emotions. If they were aware that there is a spirit world, they could return there by simply abandoning their resentment and jealousy. But the tragedy is that they do not know about the heaven in the spirit world reserved especially for aborted babies. So they are just stuck in this sad limbo.

Instead, they refuse to leave their mothers' sides for even an instant and keep crying out over and over, "Mama, mama. I'm so hungry, please give me something to eat. Let me have the same toys that older brother has."

But an answer never comes. No matter how much the unborn child's spirit calls out, no answer is ever forthcoming from the mother. So the aborted baby's spirit just sobs and sobs as he or she keeps pleading to be able to exist as was meant by Heaven.

I think anyone who has ever raised a dog or a cat can understand how these little unborn babies feel. If such pets are treated with love, then it seems as if they can almost understand what their masters say to them. If you look like you are about to go out and leave them alone, they will infer as much and do everything they can to get your attention, maybe even by doing their business. When they are hungry they will bark or meow to get you to feed them. If you lavish your attention on a little baby, they will get jealous and come over and rub themselves against you or scratch at you with their paws seeking attention.

If dogs and cats act in such a manner, it only seems natural that the spirit of an aborted baby, one of the highest forms of spirit life there is, should react so sensitively.

To be exact, since aborted babies are not flesh and blood, they cannot really call out or cry to make their wishes known. But their sensitivity results in continuous emanation of spiritual vibrations conveying their desires in an attempt to make their mother and siblings aware of their existence.

These vibrations are the cause of the spiritual interference that these aborted babies cause the living.

These spiritual problems manifest themselves in various ways. For example, they can cause a sense of psychological or emotional instability. When such a child's spirit is in the vicinity of the mother, she might suddenly become hysterical, feel emotionally very down or otherwise psychologically or emotionally unstable.

Secondly, a throbbing pain in the head will often afflict the mother, her hips will feel very tired, her eyes will dim, or she will develop some other physical problem. As I explained earlier, the spirit of an aborted baby will never leave the side of the mother. But more specifically it will attach itself to the back of her head, neck, chest or hips. And those are the places where physical problems generally develop.

Thirdly, a mother's children will often become rebellious. As I noted before, the aborted fetus nurses a grudge against the mother and jealous feelings towards living siblings. So it seeks to make these siblings become rowdy, so as to wreak revenge against the mother. Since girls tend to be more emotional than boys, these spirits can influence them relatively easily. If the girls in a family are always acting difficult with their parents, the first thing to do is ascertain whether the mother has ever had an abortion.

Not only do these fetal spirits encourage insubordination to parents; they also do their best to spark quarrels among the brothers and sisters. They seek to sow discord and cause jealousy to brim up.

I see this kind of thing fairly often at my organization World Mate. I'll walk into the office and some of our female employees will be quarreling or crying. When I ask what is the matter, they will say it was for no reason at all. It turns out they had been bickering over some trivial question. The individuals themselves do not really know how they ended up crying. But if I use my powers of extrasensory perception, I can see clearly that the spirit of one or more aborted babies was behind the whole hassle.

"Haven't there been a lot of requests for memorial services for aborted babies the last few days?"

"Yes, some 50 or 60 of them."

"Um, and that seems to be the reason why you folks are always going at each other too. Unconsoled souls of aborted children."

I remember having just this kind of conversation at the office.

In any event, this kind of pattern seems to pop up quite often. In other words, since the spirits of the aborted babies wanted to see the memorial services for their own salvation held just as quickly as possible they were sending off spiritual vibrations to shake up the people in my office and get them moving.

You have to understand that much relatively minor bickering among siblings or friends is actually attributable to such meddling on the part of spirits of aborted children.

The fourth type of spiritual barrier that we can distinguish manifests itself by a breakdown in the concentration of surviving siblings. Their minds just seem to go blank when least desired. As a result their grades in school start to plummet.

Usually one spirit is not enough to cause such results. But when three or four of them get together they can really have an adverse impact on the concentration of a living child. The reason is that their jealousy and desire for revenge causes them to hover around, substituting for each other now and then like the members of a football team, and constantly bombarding the child who is trying to study with spiritual vibrations, calling out for example "Older brother!" or "Older sister!"

For that reason even though when actually studying the material the child might have thought that he understood it perfectly, the next morning he discovers that he cannot remember a thing.

If the teacher says, "Write what you learned yesterday," the child will reply in bewilderment, "What could that have ever been?" The mind has indeed become a complete blank.

What such children learn somehow seems quickly to disappear into a black hole. They might have studied with all their might, but while doing so they simply did not have any ability to concentrate.

Why Fathers Are Left Alone

Well, by now I think you can understand in general terms how spiritual interference from spirits of aborted babies is manifested. Many of the more minor problems of mothers and surviving siblings are really caused by such interference by aborted babies in the family. But the funny thing is that male parents are not usually bothered very much by the spirits of aborted children.

No doubt some of my readers are thinking to themselves, "The father too shares responsibility for the abortion, so wouldn't it be natural that he too should be affected by the curse of an aborted baby."

That seems a very well-founded suspicion. But the answer to the question is "No." Very few fathers are affected by grudges held by fetal spirits. In fact, 90% of the time it is the mother who becomes the target of the attack.

Why should that be? The reason is that fathers simply do not have much feeling regarding the spirits of the dead children.

Although most fathers will regret that they agreed to an abortion, they do not carry the same strong emotional attachment to the unborn child as does the mother. Their sense of regret soon disappears. But the mother feels that she has given up a part of herself and therefore a poignant sense of loss remains for quite some time. Very few men are subject to such strong feelings of remorse over an extended period of time. You might say that fathers generally remain immune to the influence of the spiritual waves that the deceased fetal spirits are sending out. For that reason they are largely unaffected by the spiritual interference these waves cause.

Still, occasionally a man who knows a bit about the spiritual dimension – a brooding, soulful, sensitive type of individual – will wallow in regret, saying something like this to himself, "Oh, why did I kill that little baby. I'm so sorry. I'm so sorry."

In such cases, a special kind of spiritual channel is opened and this kind of sensitive individual becomes very susceptible to spiritual interference.

No doubt some of you are now thinking, "Well in that case, mothers too would be well advised not to take things too hard. If they don't brood on their loss, then they won't become the victim of spiritual attacks. Best to forget just as soon as possible."

That is exactly how it is. As I explained in Chapter 1 of this book, if a person has a strong will and does not pay much attention to emotion-laden things, then he or she will usually not be susceptible to spiritual interference.

For example, if a person's emotions tend to be unstable, the temples of her head often throbs with pain, or her hips feel languid, she should not jump to the conclusion that this signifies interference from the aborted child. If instead she attributes it to some physical cause, saying, "I've been run-down recently" or "It's just a menopausal disorder," the woman will not become easy prey for intensive spiritual interference.

But at the same time, bear in mind that the spirits of aborted children still are hanging around. So even if the mother remains immune to spiritual interference from her aborted fetuses, her live children may not. But more than anything else, you should remember just how pitiful the spirits of these poor aborted babies are. I always try to keep that fact in mind when I am conducting memorial services for aborted babies.

Aborted Children Go to Mars

As I noted before, when discussing memorial services for the release of suffering spirits of aborted babies, the first thing to do is to pray to the gods for forgiveness of the sin of killing the fetus. In this way, you can purify a clouded womb spirit. Since in the case of a miscarriage, the womb becomes murky through no fault of the women concerned, its spirit is really not all that cloudy and there is no need to ask for special forgiveness from the gods.

Next, you have to bring relief for the double suffering that the spirit is enduring. That will free the fetal spirit to go to the special heaven that has been prepared for such innocents.

This at least is the procedure that I follow during a memorial service for an aborted baby.

Furthermore, since the aborted baby committed absolutely no sin, his or her spirit is unconditionally welcomed into heaven. On the other hand, because the child had no opportunity to perform great spiritual works on earth, the spirit does not qualify to enter the highest levels of heaven. Still it is consoling to know that every aborted baby unconditionally has a place reserved for himself or herself in heaven. The problem is that the suffering spirit of the aborted fetus does not realize there is a home waiting, so it continues to hover around the mother bearing a grudge for the cruel way it was treated. The real purpose of the memorial service is to break this vicious circle and to release the child's spirit to journey to the heavenly world.

But how exactly is the spirit taken to heaven? I go into that point in considerable detail in *Divine Powers,* so please consult that book on this score. Here I would simply like to describe what the heaven for aborted fetuses is like. Before doing that, however, I should first give a general description of the organization of the spiritual world.

When a person dies, he sloughs off the cloak of flesh he wore in this world and sets out on a journey to the spirit world. None of us are exempt from that journey, I might add. But that does not mean that we are all headed for the same destination. We are assigned to an appropriate spirit world, depending on a final judgment made of our intentions, thoughts, good deeds and bad deeds while we were alive.

But for the first 30 years after dying we remain in a kind of limbo, a spiritual crossroads – the realm of ghosts and other lingering spirits. This in-between world goes by several different names in Japanese, but they all refer to the same spiritual state. After this transitory period is over, the spirit then sets off for the true spiritual world.

This spiritual world can be divided into three general parts: the heavenly realm, the intermediate spiritual zone and the world of hell. The heavenly realm can further be subdivided into Number One Heaven, Number Two Heaven and Number Three Heaven. Similarly, the intermediate spiritual zone and hell also have three subdivisions. And in turn, each of the subdivisions in each of these three spiritual worlds are further subdivided into many smaller pockets. And all of these spiritual kingdoms are in the spiritual universe that parallels our physical universe.

More specifically, the heavenly world is to be found on Jupiter, Venus, the Sun and the North Star. The middle to upper reaches of the intermediate spiritual zone are found on the Mercury spiritual world, and its middle and lower reaches are to be found on the Moon and Mars. Likewise, the hell zone contains Saturn and part of Neptune. Of course, I am referring to the unseen spiritual dimension of all these astral bodies. I should point out here that

Saturn is the place where souls undergo rehabilitation through spiritual training. Those who are sent here have to undergo severe training that involves much suffering of various kinds. That is why it is part of hell. On the other hand, Mercury is the place where people who are obsessed with the search for the truth, in the scientific or artistic sense are sent to. Individuals who spent their time on earth acquiring spiritual merit or living a positive, optimistic life are eligible to enter the heaven on Jupiter.

Since this spiritual Jupiter is part of heaven, anyone who is lucky enough to go there enjoys a sense of happiness and a wealth of opportunities for further spiritual development. In that sense, Jupiter is indeed the lucky planet. In addition, those people who are intent on becoming more spiritually refined, the spiritual elite if you please, go to Venus. The very best in this category will not settle for less than the spiritual world of the Sun – the deluxe spiritual world as far as brightness, optimism and refinement goes. Others, who are hungering after the ultimate in knowledge, spiritual principles or beauty, journey to the spiritual world of the North Star. As you can see, there is an appropriate spiritual level for each spirit and its needs.

On the other hand, people who lived average lives – never doing that much evil or that much good for that matter – are sent to the spiritual world of the Moon. This place is neither very light, nor very dark. It therefore makes sense that it should be in the central part of the intermediate zone.

As for those people who were very competitive and obsessed with winning while on earth, they are destined to go to Mars, which lies in the middle to lower portion of the intermediate spiritual zone.

Well then, let us return to our discussion of the spirits of the aborted children.

The heaven for these little unborn babies is to be found in the Mars spiritual world. The reason why that should be so is that the wailing of the little babies is so loud and ardent and exhibits such energy that there is a certain appropriateness that they should be sent here.

In this world an entire educational system has been established for the aborted fetus spirits and they are educated with great care. Of course, there are plenty of toys and much milk for them. It is something like a large nursery school or day care center. After these little souls have been nourished for a certain period of time and have grown to a certain extent, they are sent to the spiritual world of Mercury. This is the world where the spirits of dead infants live.

Just like on earth in the spiritual world human beings undergo growth, both physically and in terms of knowledge. So basically what happens is that after the spirits of the aborted babies reach the heavenly world, their spiritual bodies and souls undergo growth. Then when they become the spiritual equivalent of a one- or two-year-old baby, they are sent to Mercury.

Usually spirits undergo spiritual training in the spiritual world for a century or two before being reborn into the material world. In especially speedy cases, this spiritual renewal is completed in only five to six decades. Actually, in principle no spirit undergoes training for more than two centuries.

However, here I have to make an important caveat. There is the important exception of the unborn child who already has developed a true soul. If the soul already has developed to this extent, then for example after a still birth the soul will immediately take on the appearance of an elderly Buddhist monk or priest and return to the spirit world. What I was referring to above was the case of a fetus that had not developed a soul, who of its own free will forsook the material world to go to the specially designated heaven waiting for him or her on Mars. So unless aided, these children end up eternally tied to the world by their grudge towards their mothers, weeping and calling their mothers names.

That is the reason why it is so important to carry out memorial services to allow these tortured souls to depart.

A Correct Memorial Service

However, I must regretfully add that the memorial services normally carried out for aborted babies are simply not enough to do the job. In fact, the number of correctly performed memorial services of this kind are extremely few. Almost zero you might say. The reason is that the apparently simplest-to-perform spiritual purification ceremonies are really the most difficult to perform.

Of all the religious groups and psychics whom I have observed performing spiritual purifications, rarely have I found any who knew the simplest facts about the subject. For example, they are not aware that there is a heaven for the souls of the aborted children. Much less do they know how to send them there. Sorry to say, but they are simply unfit to do what they are attempting to do.

I have also reached the conclusion that if people, even when alive, investigate a little bit about the spirit world, then it is much easier for them to prepare for their life after death. Furthermore, if after having experienced a good spiritual world, they realize that there are even finer spiritual worlds in existence, these people will be stimulated into wanting to overcome the barriers separating us from those spiritual worlds of the afterlife by exerting themselves spiritually. It is for this reason that I conduct countless World Mate "Star Tours" to the spiritual universe beyond.

What we have seen on these mystical journeys very much resembles the world of Antoine St. Exupery's famous story "The Little Prince." What I see is as detailed as were his descriptions in that story. That is how I came to be intimately familiar with the heaven prepared for unborn children. I do not know anyone else alive who is as familiar with that scene as I am, although there may well be such an individual.

Anyhow it is for that reason, as I explained in *Divine Powers,* that we today have the spectacle of all kinds of people performing simply unbelievable spiritual purifications of unborn children.

Let me give a specific example about what I am talking about. It happened when I was once performing a memorial service for an aborted fetus. With my powers of clairvoyance I was able to see that there were five fetuses attached with strings like the paper dolls known as *teruterubozu* that are used to predict the weather. When I looked closely at the ends of these strings, I found that they were attached to a statue of *Jizo*, the guardian deity of children. Strange to say, just like little dogs the spirits of those five aborted fetuses were running around and around in circles about that *jizo*.

When I first saw this sight, I found it difficult to comprehend its meaning. I thought to myself, "What could this possibly be?"

But its significance quickly dawned on me. The psychic who had previously performed a spiritual purification on the mother had thought only of preventing the fetuses from continuing to harass her. He used his psycho kinetic energy to tie them down to the *jizo*.

True, the fetuses so tied down were now unable to do any mischief. But the sight was too sad for words.

When the person carrying out a spiritual purification really does not know what he is up to performs a ceremony to release aborted fetuses, it is easy to end up with some kind of travesty like this.

Say the person performing the spiritual purification is concentrating on the thought "Do not do any more mischief" or "Leave your mother and go elsewhere." If he conducts the ceremony in such a frame of mind, it will do absolutely nothing to release the aborted baby. In this connection I would like to mention the case of this kind that utterly appalled me. I heard this from the mother herself. It seems she went to some kind of place that specializes in divination. She was interested in her marriage prospects since a favorable match was pending and the fee charged by the fortuneteller there was inexpensive. So she felt quite light-spirited when she went in for a consultation.

But then things went awry. After a simple preliminary divination session, the fortuneteller asked without further ado whether she was possessed by the spirit of an aborted child. The woman was shocked because she had indeed had the baby conceived with her previous boyfriend aborted. "Well....the fact is...." she started to answer.

Then the diviner said, "If there is such a spirit around, it will seek vengeance throughout your entire lifetime. Especially when it comes to your marriage chances or love life, the spirit will do its best to mess things up. So you will never be able to make a good marriage. It is easy to predict that the aborted fetus will ruin your chances for marriage in your present case."

All this time the fortuneteller was staring at her in very stern fashion.

The woman then blurted out, "I thought this might be the situation. Please perform a spiritual purification to release the spirit."

"Well, that would seem the appropriate course of action," the diviner replied."

"How much will it cost?"

"Oh, I assure you it will not be that expensive."

"Well, then please go ahead with it."

"My assistant does these things at the rate of only ¥2,000 per day."

"Oh, I see. Thank you so very much."

"We will of course require a one year's payment of spiritual purification fees, to be presented in advance."

"A one year's payment....what does that..."

"That is ¥2,000 by 365 days or ¥730,000."

The deluded woman paid that amount of ¥730,000 the following day. All she could think about was that her chances in the pending marriage proposal would not be ruined. Later when I conducted a proper spiritual purification and freed the fetal spirit, she was overjoyed. When she was told that the fetal spirit had been released and had left her body, the woman broke down into tears of gratitude. However, as things turned out the proposed marriage did prove a no go. I can well understand how on looking back at that earlier unsuccessful phony spiritual purification and the fact that her marriage never took place, she should be filled with rage and frustration at the experience.

But this fortuneteller never had promised that he would perform a special spiritual purification to release the fetal spirit to heaven forever. He just performed a standard spiritual purification at a rate of ¥2,000 per day. No doubt he would argue that he performed a proper spiritual purification as promised and stopped the mischief by the fetus. There is nothing the woman could really say in return. Actually, what we have here is the case of an unprincipled operator preying on the weakness in a woman's heart and viciously taking advantage of her with ruthless tactics.

Well, let me get back to the main track and reiterate an important point that I made earlier. The spirits of aborted children have a two-fold state of mind. So if you really want to release their spirits, you first must find some way to deal with both these emotions.

You have to do the equivalent of giving them milk to drink and baby clothes to wear. Of course, offering real milk or clothes does no good whatsoever no matter what amounts you may use. Since these spirits of aborted fetuses are already for all practical purposes in the spirit world, you must use spiritual power that in the spirit world will provide a good taste or enjoyment to the little suffering spirits.

If you can make them satisfied enough, win over their confidence so to speak, you will be in the position to tell them about the heaven that has been prepared for them. And then you can transport them there instantaneously. If you do not release them all at once like I have just described, then you have not really performed a spiritual purification, releasing them from their attachment to the material world.

And if you do not – say for example you do a little circumscribed spiritual purification on a monthly basis – you actually will be accomplishing nothing at all.

"We're so sorry. We're so sorry. Please forgive your mother."

"Don't be jealous of your sisters anymore."

No doubt about it; prayers like these soothe the tortured souls of aborted fetuses. But the effect is only temporary. And after a while the spirit will begin to think once again, "But I'm still envious of those in the world of the living."

Think of it as something like the following situations: Say you have a dog or cat who you lavish attention on every single day. Let that animal see you making a fuss over another animal and it will be burning with jealousy. Or a woman who catches her lover sneaking a peak at foxy woman nearby. No matter how mild-mannered she might normally be, that woman's blood is going to start boiling with jealousy. It may be rude of me to compare an aborted fetus to a dog or cat. But the elemental emotions at work here are really the same.

Extremely Difficult Fetus Spiritual Purifications

It does not matter what type of spiritual purification we are talking about, whether it involves the spirit of an aborted fetus, a vengeful spirit or an ancestral spirit, at all times you must perform the ceremony in the proper spirit. You should not think that you are going to get rid of a pesky, unwanted visitor. Rather from the bottom of your heart you must dwell on how you are going to release that spirit from its present suffering by winning its compliance with what you propose. But what exactly do you need to do to accomplish this goal? You must first understand exactly how the spirit feels. That is the first step to sympathetic understanding and sincere identification.

"Oh, I can understand your desire for revenge. How hard it must be. How much you must have suffered?"

If in this fashion you do your best to understand the spirit's feelings and to sympathize with him, he is likely to reply as follows, "Thank you for understanding how I really feel. I am ready to listen to what you have to say."

In other words, the real key to performing a spiritual purification correctly is to understand what the spirit involved is feeling. But let me hasten to add that in the case of aborted fetuses it is by no means easy to gain this understanding and then to go on and completely release their spirits. Quite the opposite, it is about the most difficult thing imaginable to do. The reason is that the person performing the spiritual purification cannot totally identify with the feelings of the unborn child.

I wonder how many people are really capable of understanding the feelings of these aborted children. Even among those who realize the two-fold nature of their psychology, there must be very, very few who can truly empathize with them.

That alone should make you realize just how difficult it is to carry out a proper spiritual purification and effect the spiritual release of these little ones. Furthermore, unlike with adult spirits the aborted fetuses are incapable of knowing that there is somewhere they can go to, and even if they did they would be incapable of resolving to make the move on their own. There are just so many difficulties involved in this kind of spiritual purification. In the end you find you have to take the fetuses to the heaven awaiting them on your own – grabbing them by feet and arms, soothing and cajoling them all the way.

When the famous 16th century warlord Toyotomi Hideyoshi was asked after he had unified Japan what had been the most difficult experience in his entire life, he replied, "It was singing lullabies to little babies to try to make them sleep when I was just a little boy. Nothing thereafter was as hard."

I can sympathize with Hideyoshi's sentiments. So although the release of a fetal spirit might seem quite a simple task to the uninitiated, I would note that it is a task that I will not delegate to even the most accomplished of my personal disciples. I do every single one of these spiritual purification personally. As I explained earlier, nearly every single fetal spiritual purification performed these days is being done improperly. The difficulty involved is the reason for this phenomenon. Make no mistake about it: simply erecting a memorial tablet or having an image carved brings no salvation for the baby.

But what exactly is wrong with these other forms spiritual purification. As I explained earlier, true extrication of the aborted baby from its no win situation only occurs if you can completely win over its confidence, so that it consents to accompany you to the heaven for aborted babies and never again attempts to return to the place where its parents are.

In order for this to happen, the parents too must do their part. After the spiritual purification has been completed, they must in no case ever again dwell in their thoughts on the aborted child, hold any kind of ceremony on the anniversary of the death, or feel pity or longing for the dead baby. The reason is that if the living do not cut off all emotional attachments, then the aborted baby that has just started a brand-new, happy life in the spiritual world will have its memories of its parents dredged up and he will be drawn back towards this material world.

The plight of these aborted children is truly pitiful. And no one knows better the importance of winning them spiritual release than do the mothers involved. They truly understand the feelings of these unborn children. I would therefore advise these mothers not to go rushing off the closest clairvoyant or temple and ask them to take care of things. Better by far after going through the contents of this book carefully to place your complete trust in your local tutelary god. Talk to the spirit of the dead child. Pray for forgiveness for your sin to the tutelary god. And humbly entreat the gods to send the spirit of the dead child to the heaven for aborted babies.

Finally, I would note that although it is impossible for me to reply individually to all the letters that are sent to me by readers, I do read every single one of them. I always bear them in mind when planning my next book, since I seek to answer your questions through my books. Therefore I would ask you to please keep those cards and letters coming. I appreciate them ever so much. And of course I invite comments and criticisms of this book.

Also, any readers of this book who might be interested in the various spiritual activities being carried out through World Mate are encouraged to contact the organization directly. Informational literature will be sent to you free of charge. Until we meet again, whether it be through one of my books or other media projects, let me just wish you the best from the bottom of my heart. So long!

Toshu Fukami

WORLD MATE

World Mate is a cultural organization whose staff, beginning with its leader Toshu Fukami, are dedicated to helping people achieve the most rewarding possible lifestyle and true happiness. It does this by offering study activities that members participate in on a totally voluntary basis.

World Mate can help you get more out every facet of your life, including business, love, marriage, personal success, a cheerful way of living and health. It is, however, not interested solely in personal success, but also through its social welfare activities and similar creative means seeks to lend a helping hand to people of the world who are suffering.

You are free to join or leave World Mate as you desire. All those who are interested in achieving a fulfilling, radiant lifestyle are invited to become members.

For further information, please contact
World Mate
3-162 Tachibana Ohitocho,
Tagata-gun, Shizuoka 410-23
Japan.
Tel. 81-558-76-1060

Foreign Branches of World Mate

USA/New York Branch
World Mate New York

World Mate, Inc.
150 E. 57th St. #9D NY, NY 10022
Phone: 646-414-1366
E-mail: worldmate@rcn.com

Arizona Area
World Mate Arizona
5615N Acoma Dr. #33
Glendale, AZ 85306

Chicago Area
World Mate Chicago
#1602, 1660 N. Lasalle St.,
Chicago, IL 60614

United Kingdom/London Branch
World Mate London
am Gate,
yards Road, Cobham,
y KT11 2LA, UK

alia/Perth Branch
Mate Perth
Unit 15A, Victoria Street,
West Perth, WA6005, Australia

New Zealand Branch
Room 3, 6th Floor,
Hobson Court,
70 Hobson Street, Wellington
New Zealand

Toshu Fukami

Mr. Haruhisa Handa, whose pen name is Toshu Fukami, was born in 1951 and graduated from Doshisha University with a degree in Economics.

He is the leader of World Mate, honorary chairman of the Japanese Blind Golf Association, executive director of the International Foundation of Arts and Culture, vice president of the International Shinto Foundation, and head of B.C. Consulting – a management consulting firm.

As a small boy, he had numerous spiritual experiences. At the age of 15, he decided to dedicate his life to helping humankind. Since then he has engaged in numerous activities designed to unite the divine and human dimensions in everyday life. Before he turned 25, he had achieved extraordinary powers for seeing or hearing divine communications, looking into the hearts of other people, predicting futures, understanding the karmic influences on others and extrasensory, spiritual perception.

Among his more than 300 divinely-inspired talents are the ability to see a person's guardian spirits, tell previous lives, offer star tours and conduct ceremonies to provide relief to the spiritually afflicted. Fukami's artistic and cultural attainments have an amazing breadth, including songwriting and musical arrangement, conducting, poetry of the waka form, calligraphy, tea ceremony, Noh recitations and traditional Japanese dance. He has had numerous releases on CD and video. He is also the author of more than 30 bestselling books, including the immensely popular *Lucky Fortune*, which has sold more than 700,000 copies.

Fukami currently hosts two radio programs. He has also planned, organized and appeared in two tremendously successful charity concerts at the Royal Albert Hall in 1995 and Carnegie Hall in 1996.

Major Toshu (Seizan) Fukami Best-Sellers Are Now Available

The Lucky Fortune Series

Watch Your Luck Get Better and Better Day By Day! ───────────

Lucky Fortune

This book guides you to better luck and fortune in life. You can learn the four basic principles for getting lucky. By practicing the principles, chanting the Power Call with your eyes on a special logo mark, praying to the gods of celestial bodies as well, you can enjoy fantastic fortune in every aspect of your life!

BY TOSHU FUKAMI   ¥1,575 (tax included)

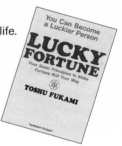

Happiness is Calling You – an Introduction to Japanese Spiritualism! ─────────

Divine Order

This book reveals some deep aspects of the origins of fortune. You will surely recognize the importance of understanding the essentials of the spirits and gods in order to acquire heavenly fortune.

BY TOSHU FUKAMI   ¥1,575 (tax included)

A truly Miraculous Spiritual Revolution! ──────────────────

Divine World

This book leads you to understand the true meaning of Life. Making use of psychic or supernatural powers provided by the gods, you can fulfill the true meaning of human existence!

BY TOSHU FUKAMI
¥1,575 (tax included)

How to Harness and Control Your Destiny ――――――――――――――――――――

Divine Powers

This book fully explains about the spiritual world and
the spiritual hindrances. It further teaches you clearly
which of the divine and spiritual powers are good,
and which of them are evil, and suggests the proper
course for divine and spiritual powers. Having a
better understanding of divine and spiritual
powers, you can put yourself on the right
course in life.

BY TOSHU FUKAMI　¥1,575 (tax included)

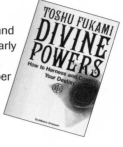

You Can Develop Spectacular Luck! ――――――――――――――――――――

Make Your Own Luck

This book guides you towards the right way to create
your own luck. With three separate perspectives of the
material, spiritual and divine worlds in your mind, you
can create luck that is three times as strong, wide-
ranging and resolute as the man who relies solely on
common sense, and attain everlasting happiness
and prosperity.

BY TOSHU FUKAMI　¥1,575 (tax included)

Your Guardian Spirits of Love Will Bring You Good Luck! ――――――――――――

Divine Help in Romance

This book leads you to improve tremendously your
luck with love, marriage and family relationships.
From a spiritual perspective, it generously offers
appropriate advice for various love-related
problems.

BY TOSHU FUKAMI　¥1,575 (tax included)

New publication by Toshu Fukami
Now on Sale!

notes

notes

大 除 霊（英語版）

平成　4年 3月25日	初　版
平成　9年 8月30日	改訂版第2版
平成10年 6月25日	改訂版第2版第2刷

著者	深 見 東 州
翻訳者	ジョン・J・キャロル
発行人	杉 田 早 帆
発行所	株式会社たちばな出版

〒167-0042 東京都杉並区西荻北3-42-19 第6フロントビル

Tel. 03 (5310) 2131　Fax. 03 (3397) 9295

| 印刷・製本 | 慶昌堂印刷株式会社 |

落丁本・乱丁本はたちばな出版販売部宛にお送り下さい。送料小社負担にてお取り替えいたします。

Once upon a time there was a fairy princess, a GIANT, an evil prince, and a bunch of dumb trees. They were all in my big sister Tina's play, The Terrific Tale of Tara, the Proud Fairy Princess. I decided to try out for the proud fairy princess. For good luck I borrowed Tina's lucky charm on the day of the tryouts. But it must've been an unlucky charm, because it only brought me and EVERYBODY bad luck. So, you see, I didn't (almost) ruin the play on my own. I had help. It's not my fault that part of my costume caused someone to SNEEZE, which caused the little saplings to giggle and the audience to laugh when they weren't supposed to! Think this can't happen to you? It can. And here's how—step by step. . . .

Willie

RULE BOOK #4

How to (Almost) Ruin Your School Play

By Valerie Wilson Wesley
Illustrated by Maryn Roos

JUMP AT THE SUN
HYPERION BOOKS FOR CHILDREN • NEW YORK

For Jackie, always a star

Text copyright © 2005 by Valerie Wilson Wesley
Illustrations copyright © 2005 by Maryn Roos

Printed in the United States of America

First Edition

3 5 7 9 10 8 6 4 2

Library of Congress Cataloging-in-Publication Data on file.

ISBN 0-7868-5259-3

Visit www.jumpatthesun.com

My Rules   Step by Step

Willimena's
Rules

STEP #1:
Have a Playwright
for a Sister

Sometimes my sister, Tina, gets all the breaks. For one thing, she's two years older than me, so she's taller and can reach things I can't. She also knows how to write cursive and multiply fractions. Most of the time, I'm not jealous of her, but sometimes I just can't help it. Like the other night at dinner, when she made her big announcement.

"Guess what, everybody!" she said as she twirled spaghetti onto her fork.

1

"My play, *The Terrific Tale of Tara, the Proud Fairy Princess*, won the school play-writing contest." Tina's grin was one of the biggest I'd ever seen on her face.

My dad put down his fork. My mom put down her glass. Even Doofus Doolittle, our cat and one of my best friends, gave a loud meow.

"That's terrific!" said my dad.

"Congratulations, Tina! I'm so proud of you," said my mom.

Doofus Doolittle jumped into Tina's lap. He put his chin next to hers and licked sauce off her cheek. Tina gave him a hug. Then she looked at me. I could see she was happy. I knew she was waiting for me to say something nice, too.

"That's great, Tina," I said. "That's good news!"

Now, don't get me wrong. I *really* did mean it. I *really* was happy for Tina. I had a *really* big smile on my face. But there was a teeny-weeny, itsy-bitsy spot inside of me that didn't mean it all *that* much.

"And guess what else, everybody! Guess what else!" Tina said. "I get to help Mrs. White direct the play and decide who will be in it."

"We're so happy for you!" my mom and dad said together, like they were the same person.

"What are the roles?" asked my dad.

"Well, there's Max, the wise giant, who is big and tall. He's the oldest person in the play," said Tina. "There are four elves, who are tiny and cute. Igor is the mean, evil prince, who does bad things, and there's the star of the play. Her name is

Tara, and she is the proud fairy princess. There are also a lot of trees."

"Trees? How come there are trees in your play?" Putting trees in a play sounded dumb to me, but I didn't say it. Trees are usually painted on the back of the stage. They're just scenery.

"I wanted a lot of kids to be in my play, so I made the trees characters," Tina said.

"That was such a good idea," said my dad.

"What a thoughtful thing to do!" said my mom.

Doofus Doolittle rubbed up against Tina and purred.

"Who would want to play a dumb tree?" I said.

Tina looked hurt. "Lots of kids."

"What do the trees say?"

"Nothing, of course. They're trees! That's a dumb question, Willie. Have you ever heard a tree talk?"

Suddenly, the *old* Tina was back. That's the Tina who reminds me she's my older sister. The one who bosses me around and likes to get her way.

"Don't call me dumb, Tina!" I said. "It's dumb to have a dumb play with a bunch of dumb trees standing around!"

My mom and dad looked at each other. Then they looked at me and Tina.

"Girls, don't start calling each other names," my mom said.

"I don't want any fighting tonight," my dad said.

"She started it by saying my play was dumb," Tina said. I could tell she was hurt.

I was sorry I had said it. But I wasn't ready to tell Tina yet.

"But you called me dumb," I said instead.

"Apologize," my mom said.

"Her first," Tina said.

"Sorry," I said.

"Me, too," said Tina. Nobody spoke for a while. Even Doofus Doolittle was quiet.

Finally, my mom asked, "Can everybody in the whole school try out for the play?"

"Anybody who is a good actor."

"Willie is a very good actor!" my dad said. "Remember when Willie was the frog in that play a few years back?"

"Yes, she was great!" my mom added.

"She was the best frog I ever saw," Tina said. I knew she was trying to make up. My whole family was trying to make me feel better. I tried to smile, but somehow it just wouldn't come. For one thing, the frog play had happened a long time ago. I was in kindergarten, and all I had to do was sit, croak, and pretend to catch flies.

"You were *so* cute with your green face and green tights," my mom said with a smile.

"And you certainly did some of the best croaking I've ever heard!" added my dad.

"I was so proud of you!" Tina said.

There are times when your family knows just what to say to make you feel better. *This* was not one of those times.

My dad turned back to Tina. "So who do you want to be in your play?"

"Well," Tina said in a serious voice, "the giant has to be one of the sixth graders because he or she has to be bigger than anybody else. The cute little elves will be in kindergarten or first grade. Igor, the evil prince, should probably be a boy, but a girl can play him, too. And of course the best part, the part of Tara, the proud fairy princess, will have to be someone who is very, very special."

"I'll bet every girl in the whole school will want to play that part," my mom said.

"Mrs. White said we should choose a girl in the third grade."

Third grade? That was *my* grade!

"The proud fairy princess is very smart but sometimes she gets into trouble. She's a good person, but sometimes she does the wrong thing. She tries to help people, but sometimes she gets them into more trouble. But her heart is always in the right place. Her one fault is that she's very proud."

Except for the proud stuff, Tara sounded like somebody I knew.

Me!

Without even reading Tina's play, I knew the role I wanted, and I was sure I couldn't miss. Even though Tina and I fought a lot, when things were bad, she was always in my corner. I could usually count on her to help me out when I needed it most. There were times when my sister could turn into my very best friend. A smile spread across my face. Suddenly I knew that things would be all right. With my sister's help, I could hop from frog to fairy princess in one short lifetime!

STEP #2:
Beg for the Starring Role

Before I got dressed for bed that night, I wrote in my journal:

I hope I will be the star of Tina's play.

I wrote it ten times down the middle of the page. I didn't know if that would do any good, but I thought I'd try it anyway. Then I remembered what my grandma said about positive thinking. Positive thinking means believing that the *best* will happen instead of the *worst*.

So I crossed out "I hope" on the page and drew a line under *will*. Now it read:

~~I hope~~ <u>I WILL</u> be the star of Tina's play.

That felt better.

After my mom turned out the lights, I said to Tina, "I *really* want to be the proud fairy princess in your play."

Tina didn't answer.

"Did you hear me?" I sat up and looked over at her bed. She had pulled the blanket over her head. She does that when she doesn't want to talk.

"Please, Tina. With chocolate sprinkles on top."

Tina pulled down her blanket. She climbed out of her bed and sat down on mine. When she put her arm around me,

I got a bad feeling. Tina only does that when she is about to tell me something I don't want to hear.

"Willie, I can't pick you to be the star just because you're my sister," she said.

"But kids pick best friends to do special stuff all the time, and being sisters is better than being best friends. It's *your* play. Why can't you do it?"

"It wouldn't be fair. You have to try out like everybody else."

"But what if I don't get the part I want?"

"Well, a lot of kids won't get the parts they want."

"But I really want it, and I know I'm the best person."

"A lot of kids think they're the best person," Tina said.

"Can't you just help me a little bit," I said. "We *are* sisters! Please? Please? Please?"

I can count on two fingers the number of times I've begged Tina for something. Twice. The first time was three years ago when I begged her to give me a ride on her new bike. The second time was six months ago when I asked her not to tell Mom I broke her blue glass vase. Neither time worked.

"That wouldn't be fair, Willie." Tina's voice was serious. I knew she meant it.

"Please, Tina!" This would be the third time. It really hurt.

Tina sighed a heavy sigh.

"You are my sister, I guess," she said, like maybe she wasn't so sure about it. "I'll tell you what I'm going to do." She turned on the lamp near her bed and went into her backpack. She pulled out a blue folder marked THE TERRIFIC TALE OF TARA, THE PROUD FAIRY PRINCESS and gave it to me.

"This is a copy of my play. Mrs. White gave me an extra one when she ran it off this afternoon. I'm going to give it to you so you can have a head start rehearsing for the role. I guess that will be okay. But don't tell anyone, and don't ask me for anything else!"

"Thank you, Tina. Thank you so much! I'm going to work really hard. I hope I get it! I hope I do!"

"Don't worry, Willie. You'll do fine!" Tina said.

I gave my sister a big hug. Then I put *The Terrific Tale of Tara, the Proud Fairy Princess* under my pillow. Maybe the words would creep into my head while I slept.

The next day at school, Mrs. Sweetly gave all the kids in my class a copy of Tina's play.

"I want you all to read and study the part you want to play," she said. "Everyone will have a chance to try out."

I was proud to see Tina's name on the cover. It made me glad that Tina was my sister. But I could always count on Crawford Mills to turn my pride into pain.

"Tina Thomas! Isn't that silly Willie Thomas's crazy sister?" he cried out. Everybody started to laugh.

"I hate you, Crawford Mills!" I whispered to myself.

"Crawford, I don't want to hear that!" said Mrs. Sweetly with a scowl. She stood up and shook her finger at Crawford Mills.

He sank down into his seat. That made me feel better. "Willie should be very proud of her sister, and I'm sure she is. Tina Thomas has written a very good play."

Mrs. Sweetly wrote in big letters on the blackboard:

PLAY TRYOUTS NEXT MONDAY!

I opened my copy of Tina's play and imagined myself dressed as Tara, the proud fairy princess.

Everybody in my class was excited about the play and wanted to be in it. Mrs. Sweetly said that we should all try out for all the roles. Most of the girls wanted to play Tara, the proud fairy princess. Most of the boys wanted to play Igor, the mean, evil prince.

Every chance I got, I tried to memorize Princess Tara's lines. I'd read them out loud, then close my eyes and try to see the words in my mind. Then I'd say them out loud again. I whispered them to myself while I rode the bus to school. I practiced them when I ate my lunch. I sang them in the tub as I took my bath. I wrote them down before I went to bed at night.

Most of the lines in the play were spoken by Princess Tara and Prince Igor. Max, the wise giant, and the cute little elves didn't have much to say. The trees, which included saplings, weeping willows, and oaks, just stood on stage. Princess Tara and Prince Igor talked mostly to each other. I had to learn Igor's lines so I could learn Tara's. By the end of the week, I practically knew the whole play by heart.

On Saturday morning, all the kids on my block gathered in the Greenes' backyard like we did every Saturday. But things were different this time. We weren't just there to play. Next Monday we would be competing in the big tryouts. All the kids

who went to my school wanted a role in Tina's play.

When Tina and I walked into the Greenes' backyard everybody crowded around us. It was like we were giving away chocolate-chip cookies.

"Tina, you wrote the best play I've ever read," said Gregory Greene. He was trying out for the part of Max, the wise giant.

"You're so lucky that Tina is your big sister. I wish I had a sister like Tina," said Pauline. She was trying out for Princess Tara.

Even Betty and Booker, the youngest kids on our block, got into the act. They were trying out for the parts of the cute little elves.

"Tina, I saved this for you from lunch," said Betty as she handed Tina a peppermint lollipop.

"I made this for you at school," said Booker. He gave Tina a card covered with her name surrounded by blue and silver stars.

Everybody was treating Tina like she

was a big-time movie star because they wanted her to choose them.

It was disgusting!

"Thank you, everybody. Thank you all so much," said Tina, as if she were on TV. She popped the lollipop into her mouth and handed me Booker's card.

"Hold this for me, Willie," she said, as if I were her servant.

"Don't boss me around, Tina! Hold it yourself!" I said.

"You shouldn't talk to your big sister like that, silly Willie," said Crawford Mills. He was trying out for the part of Igor, the mean, evil prince.

"Mind your own business, Crawford," I said.

"Children, children, let's have some peace!" Tina said, sounding like a grown-up.

She even looked like she'd grown a couple of inches.

"You are all my dear friends, and I'd just like to wish everyone here the very best of luck on Monday in the big tryout! You all have my best wishes. All I can say is: have fun, everyone, and may the best actors win."

She blew everybody a kiss. Then she took a bow.

I couldn't believe what I was seeing. Winning that contest had gone straight to my sister's head. But the crazy part was, everybody started to clap!

At the end of the day, though, I was no better than anybody else.

"Tina, *please, please* stick up for me when I try out for Princess Tara on Monday!" I said before we went to sleep. After the way everybody had acted in the Greenes' backyard, I thought a little more begging might improve my chances.

As usual, Tina didn't answer. Maybe she didn't hear me. Or maybe she just didn't want to.

STEP #3:
A. Borrow Your Sister's Lucky Charm
B. Lose Your Sister's Lucky Charm

"Can I borrow the good-luck charm Teddy gave you?" I asked Tina on Monday morning. Teddy is our cousin. His good-luck charm is a four-leaf clover in a plastic case. The last time Teddy visited us, the charm had brought him good luck. It helped him catch a big fish. Maybe it would help me "catch" the role of Tara, the proud fairy princess.

Tina looked doubtful. "I might need it myself."

"You've already had good luck. You won the play contest!"

"Why don't you wear your lucky red socks?"

"I have them on, but I need a double dose," I said.

"Don't you dare lose it," Tina said as she gave me it to me. I could tell she really didn't want to do it. I knew how important it was to her, and I wondered if I should take it. But I needed every bit of luck I could get.

"I promise to keep it safe."

"You'd better," Tina said in a scary voice. Her eyes were narrow. Her lips were tight. It was Tina's meanest look. There was no telling what she would do to me if I lost it. Tina had glued a safety pin on the back of her charm so she could wear it on her clothes instead of carrying it. I pinned the charm on my purple sweater. It looked a little weird, but I didn't care. I just hoped it would do its job.

When I walked into my class, everybody was gathered in the front of the room.

TRYOUTS FOR MAJOR CHARACTERS THIS AFTERNOON! was written in big letters on the blackboard.

Nearly all the kids in my class were excited about trying out for the play. Everyone was talking at once.

"Sit down now, boys and girls!" said Mrs. Sweetly. "We have work to do today. The children who want to try out for the play will go to the auditorium after lunch."

The morning seemed to go on forever. Everything was in slow motion. It took one kid an hour to read a sentence. Even simple stuff like adding 25 and 10 took forever to do. When Mrs. Sweetly asked for the capital of the United States, somebody said it was New York City. Everybody was like me—too nervous to think straight.

After lunch, Mrs. Sweetly gave the kids who wanted to try out for the play a pass to go to the auditorium.

"My last name is Starr, and I know I'm going to be Tara, the proud fairy princess," said Lilac Starr. She was first in line. Some people think Lilac will grow up to be a movie star. Last year, she got more Valentine's Day cards than anybody else in the whole second grade. But a lot of kids say she's stuck-up. Sometimes she's nice to me, like when my mom puts extra cookies in my lunch bag. Most of the time she's not.

"I hope I get the part of Igor, the mean, evil prince," said Bill Taylor. He had his fingers crossed like I did.

Crawford Mills didn't say anything. He just looked down at his feet.

I was surprised that Crawford Mills was trying out for the play. It didn't seem like something he'd want to do.

"Good luck, Willie," he muttered as we walked to the auditorium. That surprised me, too.

When we came into the auditorium, each class sat in a different row. Betty and Booker and the other kids from kindergarten and first grade were in the front row. They were all trying out for cute little elves. Kids in the third grade, like me, who were trying out for Tara and Igor, were in the second row. There were only about four sixth graders trying out for Max, the wise giant. One was Gregory Greene. When he saw me he waved, and I waved back.

At first, I didn't see Tina and Mrs. White, but then I spotted Tina in the last row. She grinned and gave me the *okay* sign. That made me feel good. It meant my sister was rooting for me.

Mrs. White came to the front of the room and climbed up on the stage. "I hope that everybody has been studying hard," she said. "This afternoon we will have try-outs. Tomorrow we will announce over the PA system who got the parts."

Everybody in the room clapped when she said that.

"I would like all the people who are trying out to come onstage. To help you get into character, I have costumes that I want each of you to wear when you read or recite your lines."

The costumes for the cute little elves were bright red-and-orange stocking caps. The one for Max, the wise giant, was a black wooden cane. Igor, the mean, evil prince, wore a cardboard crown made of daggers. A grin spread across my face when I saw the costume for Tara. It was a long, blue velvet cape with white lace on the edges. I could hardly wait to put it on.

I could see that Booker and Betty were nervous when they came onstage. Booker put his cap on backward. Everybody laughed except me. I knew how he felt. I wondered how he would feel if his sister got a part in the play and he didn't. I knew he would be happy for her. But I also knew there might be a teeny-weeny spot inside of him that would be jealous, too.

Finally it was time for the third graders. The boys who wanted to play Igor had to go first. Everyone did a good job. But Crawford Mills was the only boy who knew all the lines. He must have been studying as hard as I had. I wondered if he knew Tara's lines as well as I knew Igor's.

Because Lilac Starr's name begins with an S and mine begins with a T, she tried out first. When she came up on the stage, she walked very slowly, like she had all the time in the world. It was as if she expected everyone to wait for her. She held her head high. She looked straight ahead, like she didn't want to see any-

body. When she picked up the blue cape,
she tossed it around her shoulders like it
belonged to her. I smiled to myself. There
was no way Lilac Starr would get the part.
She was acting too stuck-up.

Then it was my turn.

When somebody in a cartoon gets scared, their knees shake. They can't swallow. Their lips won't move. Once upon a time, I laughed when that happened to cartoon people. Never again! That was how I felt when it was my turn. I was so scared, I couldn't move.

"Willie Thomas!" I heard somebody say. "Is Willie Thomas here?"

I couldn't answer. I couldn't move my feet. Then Crawford gave me a shove, and the next thing I knew, I was standing right in the middle of the stage. I didn't know whether to thank Crawford or yell at him.

"Are you ready, Willie?" asked Mrs. White.

"Yes," I said. Then my mind went blank.

"Maybe you should put on the cape," she said.

I took off my sweater and slipped on the

cape. I pulled the cape around me. I closed my eyes. The first line of the play was said by Prince Igor. When I said his first line to myself, all the others suddenly came back. Somehow, I got them all out.

I tried not to look at anybody when I went back to my seat.

"That was good, Willie!" Betty and Booker said together as I passed their row.

I couldn't believe what I was hearing. Were they teasing me?

"You did okay!" Gregory said with a wink on his way to the stage.

When the tryouts were over and we were going back to class, Tina ran over and gave me a hug. Even Crawford Mills gave me a pat on my back.

Suddenly I felt better. Maybe I hadn't been so bad, after all. Maybe I had just imagined the worst. The good-luck charm must have worked.

That was when I remembered my sweater. I must have left it on the stage! I broke out of line and ran back into the auditorium. I didn't care if I got into trouble. I climbed onto the stage and looked around for it. But my sweater, with Tina's good-luck charm pinned on it, was gone.

STEP #4:
If YOUR Part Goes to a Stuck-up Kid—Make Like a Tree and LEAVE!

Wherever it was, the good-luck charm was working. Luck was with me when I got home from school. Tina was so excited about her play, she forgot to ask me what had happened to it. She did all the talking during dinner, mostly about her play. I didn't have much to say. It was Tina's night to do the dishes, so after I did my homework, I took my bath early and went straight to bed.

"Are you feeling okay, Willie? You hardly said anything during dinner," my mom asked when she came to kiss me good night. I could tell she was worried.

"I'm fine, Mom. I'm just tired," I said, faking a yawn.

"Well, try to get a good night's sleep. Tomorrow you'll find out if you'll be playing Tara, the proud princess."

When Tina came into the room, I closed my eyes tight.

"Willie, are you still awake?" Tina asked from her bed.

I pretended to be asleep. I was afraid she would ask about her good-luck charm. The next morning, I got up before Tina, ate my breakfast fast, and got on the bus before Tina did. Tina likes to sit in the back of the bus. I sat behind the bus driver. When the bus reached the school, I jumped off the moment it stopped and ran straight to the Lost and Found in the principal's office. My fingers were crossed the whole time.

"My, Willie, you've come in bright and early," said Mrs. Morris, the principal. "You must have lost something very important to come to the Lost and Found this early in the day." Mrs. Morris pulled out a large cardboard box marked LOST AND FOUND. The box was crammed to the top with junk. There were at least fifty mismatched gloves and mittens. Most of them had holes. There were about twenty broken barrettes and a long, red-and-white-striped scarf. Pushed into one corner was a teddy bear with a torn ear. It made me sad to see him there. If I hadn't

been so worried about Tina's good-luck charm, I would have asked Mrs. Morris where he would go if nobody claimed him. I would have loved to take him home. But I was too worried to think about that now.

"What are you looking so hard for,

Willie? Maybe I can help you," Mrs. Morris said.

"My purple sweater."

"So many children forget sweaters, I have a special box just for those." She went into her office and came back with a plastic box filled with neatly folded sweaters. I spotted mine right on top. I was saved! I pulled it out and quickly slipped it on. But Tina's good-luck charm wasn't where I'd pinned it. All that was left were two tiny pinholes.

"Oh, no!" I said, pointing to the spot where it had been pinned. "I had a good-luck charm right here!"

"Was it pinned to your sweater?" Mrs. Morris asked. I could tell she was concerned. "The safety pin must have popped open, and it must have fallen off," she said.

All I could do was nod. I was afraid to trust my voice. Tina's lucky charm could be anywhere in the school. Chances were I'd never find it again.

I went back to Mrs. Sweetly's class with my head hanging low. Could things get any worse?

You bet they could.

I was so worried about losing Tina's good-luck charm, I'd almost forgotten that Mrs. White would make an announcement about the roles in Tina's play. At the end of the day, her voice boomed out over the PA system.

"Attention, all children who tried out for roles in *The Terrific Tale of Tara, the Proud Fairy Princess*," she said.

All the kids stopped what they were doing. Everybody looked up at the speaker as if Mrs. White was going to step out of it. For three minutes, I actually forgot about Tina's good-luck charm. I could see myself onstage, wrapped in Tara's cape, smiling down at the audience. I could see myself taking bows. I could hear the applause.

My happiness lasted for exactly 180 seconds. I know, because somewhere inside my head, I counted every measly one. That was how long it took Mrs. White to announce who got the roles.

She started with the youngest kids. I guess she didn't want to keep them waiting.

"The roles of the four cute little elves will be played by Jennifer Greene, Ford Baldwin, and Booker and Betty Carter," Mrs. White said.

"That's great! That's great!" I screamed out loud. I had a big grin on my face. I was so glad for Booker and Betty, I wanted to stand up and cheer.

"The part of Igor, the mean evil prince, will be played by Crawford Mills, from Mrs. Sweetly's third-grade class," said Mrs. White.

"Wow!" Crawford said. "I got it! I got it!"

Everybody started to clap. Everyone was happy for Crawford, even me. Secretly, though, I wished that another kid had gotten the role. As Tara, the proud fairy princess, I wasn't looking forward to spending a lot of time talking to Crawford Mills.

"And Mrs. Sweetly must have some very good actors in her class," continued Mrs. White. "Bill Taylor will be Crawford's understudy. That means that he will play the role if Crawford can't.

"And we have yet another member of Mrs. Sweetly's class who will be in the play," Mrs. White continued.

My heart jumped. I tried to keep my lips from trembling. Sometimes that happens when my smile gets too big.

"The role of Tara, the proud fairy princess, will be played by Lilac Starr."

I couldn't believe my ears! I sat stiff in my chair, too shocked to move. How could this happen? Mrs. White read out who would play the part of Lilac's understudy, but I didn't even hear it.

"I knew I would probably get it!" I heard Lilac say to the kid sitting next to her. "I usually get what I want."

Of all the kids who tried out for the role, why did it have to go to Lilac Starr? Wasn't it enough that she got more cards

The role of Tara, the proud fairy princess, will be played by Lilac Starr.

than anybody else on Valentine's Day? And now she was getting the role of a lifetime! The one I was supposed to play. How unfair could life be? Some people were always the princesses, never the frogs!

I almost didn't hear Mrs. White say that

Max, the wise giant, would be played by Gregory Greene. I was happy for Gregory, but I couldn't manage a smile.

"I would like to thank everyone who tried out for the major parts," Mrs. White continued. "As you all know, there are other roles in the play. These are the roles of the trees. The saplings, the weeping willows, and the oaks. Tina and I would like all of the children who tried out for the play to have these roles. The saplings will be played by first graders. The weeping willows will be played by third and fourth graders, and the oaks will be played by the fifth graders. Although the trees don't have speaking roles, they are a very important part of the play."

Then Mrs. White read the names of the kids who would play the parts of trees. She must have said my name, but I didn't hear it. I had my hands over my ears. I didn't want to hear anything else. A couple of kids gave me strange looks. I didn't care!

When school was over, I grabbed my books and dashed out of the room. I didn't care what people thought or how I looked. I didn't even care about finding Tina's good-luck charm. All I could think about was how bad I felt.

A tree? A tree!

STEP #5:
Remember:
One Push + One Shove
= Trouble!

By the time I got on the bus, I was sad instead of mad. It was hard to be happy for Betty and Booker when I saw them.

"Congratulations, you two. I'm so glad you're going to be cute little elves," I managed to say.

"Thanks, Willie," said Betty.

"What about you, Willie? Are you going to be Tara, the proud fairy princess?" asked Booker.

I didn't say anything. I just looked out the window. I guess he hadn't heard that Lilac Starr, not me, was going to be playing the part of Tara. Mrs. Cotton, our babysitter, didn't make things any easier when I got home.

"Remember to wipe your feet, Little Thomases. Don't forget to wash your hands if you pet the little animal."

"His name is Doofus Doolittle," I snapped back.

"No candy today, only fruit!" Mrs. Cotton said as she snatched away the cookie I'd saved from my lunch and handed me and Tina apples.

"Yes, Mrs. Cotton," Tina said in the cheerful voice she pulls out when she wants to get on Mrs. Cotton's good side. She could tell I was feeling bad, and she didn't want me to say anything that would get me in trouble. Sometimes my sister really looks out for me.

And then there are those other times.

When Mrs. Cotton went into the kitchen, Tina squeezed down beside me on the couch. She took a big bite of her apple. Still thinking about my cookie, I took a small bite of mine.

"I'm really sorry you didn't get the part, Willie," Tina said.

"But why didn't I get it, Tina? What happened?" I felt like crying. I hoped Tina couldn't tell.

"Willie, do you really want me to tell you the truth, even though it will hurt your feelings?"

"I can take it." After the day I'd had, I thought I could take just about anything. Boy, was I wrong!

"Well, Willie, Lilac Starr was just *better* than you," she said.

"What do you mean, *better* than me?" Considering how well I know my sister, that was a dumb thing to ask.

"Well, Lilac acted just like a real princess," Tina said. "Lilac held her head high, just like a real princess. She walked across the stage, just like a real princess. She threw the cape over her shoulders, just like a real princess. She did every-thing *just like a real princess*!"

"But I knew all the princess's lines," I said. "I knew everybody's lines!"

Tina gave a long, exaggerated sigh. "I hate to bring this up, Willie, but do you remember what happened yesterday?"

Suddenly the whole miserable experi-ence came back to me in Technicolor. Leave it to Tina to add the sound effects.

"Well, you were the worst person who tried out. You mumbled your lines like you had marbles in your mouth. You stumbled onto the stage like you were walking in your sleep. You—"

"Crawford pushed me onto the stage!" I said in a small voice.

Tina continued as if she hadn't heard me. "You had your eyes closed practically the whole time. Everybody felt sorry for you. If you hadn't been my sister, I—"

"Shut up! I've heard enough!" I said, putting my hands over my ears.

"Well, you wanted to know, and I told you," Tina said with a shrug.

"You're just being mean," I said.

"Well, I'm sorry your feelings are hurt," Tina said, taking another bite out of her apple. "But that's what happened."

"I know you, Tina. You're not really sorry!" I said.

"Think what you want. But look on the bright side: at least you'll be a tree!" Tina picked up the remote and turned on the TV.

Maybe it was because the cartoon characters were laughing when I was feeling sad. Maybe it was because my feelings were hurt, and my sister just didn't care. Maybe it was just one more bad thing on a bad day. All I know is that I gave Tina such a hard push, she fell off the couch. She looked surprised, then got up and shoved me back as hard as she could. I shoved her again. She shoved me back and added a slap on my leg. I slapped her leg and added a punch on her arm. And before we knew it, we were in a fight!

"Stop, Little Thomases! Stop! Stop! Stop!" Mrs. Cotton yelled, running into the living room and waving her hands in the air. "Well, I never! I never! I never!" If Tina and I hadn't been so angry at each other, it would have made us giggle. "You! Go to your father's study! Now!" she said as she grabbed Tina by the arm and led her to the stairs. Then she turned to me. "You! Go to your bedroom! Right this moment!" she said, pointing toward the stairs. "And neither of you can come down until your parents get home!"

Tina and I didn't look at each other as we headed off in different directions. I already felt bad about the fight. Maybe Tina really hadn't meant to hurt my feelings. Maybe she had just told me the truth, like she said. It wasn't her fault that I didn't get the part.

I tried to sneak a look at her to let her know I was sorry, but she was staring straight ahead. So I stared straight ahead, too. When she got to my father's study, she slammed the door closed. I slammed the bedroom door, too.

Tina got the better deal. There was a TV in my dad's study. I heard her turn it on. All I had was my backpack. I hadn't even brought my apple. I fished around in my backpack to see if I could find something interesting to do. There was nothing except my homework, and I didn't feel like studying. Finally, I opened my journal and started to write.

Today stinks! I'm stuck in my crummy room. I didn't get the part of Tara, the proud fairy princess. I lost Tina's good-luck charm. It wasn't on my sweater where I pinned it. I started a fight, and now Tina is mad at me. But she's really going to be mad when she finds out what I did!

Mrs. Cotton was gone by the time my

dad called me and Tina downstairs for dinner. I could tell by the scowl on his face that he was angry at us for fighting. Afterward my mom called us into the living room for a family meeting. Neither of my parents was smiling.

"Your father and I have decided to put you both on punishment for a week and a half for what happened this afternoon," my mom said.

"But Willie started it because I told her the truth about why she didn't get the part in the play!" Tina said.

All I could do was pout. My mom looked at me, then sighed.

"Willie, I'm very sorry that you didn't get the part in the play, but that is no reason to fight," she said. Then she looked at Tina. "I don't care who started it, Tina.

You're old enough to know better and understand how disappointed Willie must have been."

Neither of us said anything. Doofus Doolittle jumped into my lap and licked my chin. I could tell he was trying to make me feel better. I gave him a hug. Then he jumped down and ran over to Tina. He rubbed against her leg. Tina picked him up and hugged him, too.

"There will be no TV while you are on punishment," my dad said. "When you come home from school, Tina, you will go to my study, and Willie, you will go to your room."

"But that's not fair!" I said. "There is a TV in your study, and Tina's going to watch it!"

Tina gave me one of her meanest stares.

If looks could kill, I would have been dead meat.

"I'll take the TV out of my study, and both of you can read or do homework until dinner," my dad said. "Maybe in a week and a half the two of you will appreciate each other's company. Maybe then you'll both understand how *lucky* you are to be sisters."

Why did he have to say *that* word!

"Tell Willie I want my lucky charm back," Tina said. "Willie borrowed it, and she still has it."

My mom and dad looked at me for an answer.

"It's still in school," I said, avoiding everybody's eyes.

Well, that *was* the truth. I just didn't know where in school it was!

STEP #6:
Make Sure Your Costume Annoys the Stuck-up Star

Lucky for me, Tina was so busy worrying about her play over the next week and a half, she only asked about her lucky charm once.

"I'm so-o-o sorry, Tina. It's still in school!" I said, stirring my oatmeal. I couldn't look her in the eye.

"And just when do you plan to bring it home?" She gulped down her juice.

"Soon."

"You'd better. I'll need it Friday for

opening night. Don't you dare forget it again!"

That was on Monday. All I could do was hope for the best. I had been checking the Lost and Found every morning. Whenever I walked down the halls, I looked down at the floor. Nothing had turned up. Sooner or later I'd have to face the music.

Each morning, Mrs. Sweetly asked Crawford and Lilac to tell the class how rehearsals had gone the day before. Crawford talked about how much he loved to act, and how nervous he was about opening night. Lilac told us how excited she was, and that she couldn't wait to wear the beautiful costume.

I also heard about the play at dinner. Every night, Tina told my mom and dad the good and bad things that had happened during rehearsal. Lilac and Crawford were doing good jobs, she said, and she was proud of all the little elves. But she was worried about Bill Taylor, Crawford's understudy. He hadn't learned his lines yet.

"What will happen if Crawford gets sick and can't go on?" she asked my mom in a worried voice.

"Try not to worry about things before they happen," my mom said. "Everything will turn out fine, you'll see!"

"Think positive!" I said, which made Tina smile. It was great to see my sister smiling at me. I really missed talking and laughing with her. Being on punishment for a week and a half was really rotten. When we came home from school, we went our separate ways. Tina took her homework into dad's study. I took mine into our bedroom. Tina was working hard on her play, so she always took her bath first and was usually asleep by the time I took my bath. In the morning, Tina looked over her notes about her play. I talked to Doofus Doolittle. On the bus, Tina talked to Betty, Booker, or Crawford Mills about rehearsals. I gazed out the window.

The week went by quickly. Before I knew it, it was Thursday, the day before opening night. On Friday afternoon, there would be a dress rehearsal before the whole school. Everybody, including us, the trees, would get to wear our costumes. Friday night was the big one. That was the night everyone's parents would come. Our principal had even invited the superintendent of schools. Even the teachers were excited.

Thursday morning, Mrs. White made an

announcement over the PA system.

"Now is the time for the trees to join the play rehearsal," she said. "I want all children who will play trees to come to the auditorium after lunch."

There were twelve kids who were playing

trees. Three first graders were saplings. Three fifth graders were oaks. The rest of us were weeping willows.

When the trees joined the other actors onstage, Mrs. White said she had marked the spots where she wanted us to stand with an X. Each X had our name printed on it. The saplings would sit cross-legged on the fake grass in front of the actors. The oaks would stand in the back with their arms—excuse me—limbs crossed in front of them. The weeping willows were placed around Tara, the proud fairy princess, and Igor, the mean, evil prince. We were the only trees who would move. We would sway to the left and right, on cue. There were two rows of weeping willows. One row stood right next to the princess and prince. The others stood closer to the oaks.

I searched for the X with my name written on it and found it in the front row next to Tara, the proud fairy princess, otherwise known as Lilac Starr.

"You're standing too close to me," Lilac said when I took my place beside her.

"But this is where Mrs. White put my X," I explained, glancing down at my feet to make sure. I was standing directly on top of it. Anybody could see that.

"I don't care where your X is, you have to move back," Lilac said.

"Why?"

"Because the audience won't be able to see my face."

"What makes you think the audience wants to see *your* face?" asked Miles Washington, who was one of the oaks. He lived two streets down from me. Kids from our neighborhood always stand up for each other. He was standing behind me and gave me a grin and a wink when I turned around.

"Because I'm the star of this play!" Lilac said with a proud shake of her head.

"But, Lilac, what makes you think people won't be able to see you?" I tried to sound polite, even though I wasn't feeling that way.

"Have you *seen* your costume yet?"

I could tell by her voice I probably didn't *want* to see it.

"Well, it's covered with disgusting, crepe-paper leaves that go all over the place. When you move they will probably hit me in the face. I have allergies. The dust they stir up might make me sneeze! So move back more!" she said with a wave of her hand.

"Okay." I took another step back. I sure didn't want to make anybody sneeze.

"Not far enough! You have to leave room for your leaves."

This time, I moved back so far I bumped into Miles. That was when he spoke his fateful words.

"Trees are more important to the earth than grouchy fairy princesses," he said to one of the other oaks. "Trees should be the stars! Trees rule the world!" The other fifth graders laughed and gave each other high fives.

Lilac threw them all mean looks. "Mind your own business. And anyway, trees are *never* stars!" She turned back to me. "You're still standing too close, Willie."

This time I stood my ground. "I am *not* moving again!"

"Mrs. White!" Lilac raised her hand and waved it to get Mrs. White's attention. "Could you come here for a moment, please!"

Mrs. White came onstage. "What's wrong, Lilac?" Mrs. White looked like she had a lot on her mind. I felt bad that Lilac was bothering her with this.

"Willie is too close to me. Her costume's going to be big and clumsy. I'm afraid she will bump into me, and the audience won't hear me speak."

Mrs. White glanced at the X on the floor. Then she looked back at Lilac. Then she looked at me.

"You're okay, Willie. Just stay where you are," she said, shaking her head as she rushed off the stage.

The problem was, I didn't know whether

she meant "Just stay where you are" *before* or *after* Lilac ordered me to move!

Since it was the day before dress rehearsal, and some of the actors still didn't know their lines, Mrs. White didn't take much time with the trees. She sent us back to our classrooms early.

"You all will do fine," Mrs. White said. "You know where to stand and when to sway, and that's enough. I'll see you tomorrow at the dress rehearsal. Come early so you can get into your costumes!"

That night, Tina was still awake when I got in my bed. She had a frown on her face, and I could tell she was worried. "What if my play doesn't go well tomorrow? What if everything goes wrong?"

"Think positive!"

"Willie, did you forget the good-luck charm again? I really need it now," she said after a couple of minutes. She didn't sound angry or sad, just worried. I pulled the covers over my head and pretended to be asleep.

STEP #7:
Dream of Being a Star

I should know by now that when I dream that something good will happen, something else is on the way. For example, a while back when I dreamed that Doofus Doolittle was playing chopsticks on the piano, the pet show Tina and I were planning turned into a disaster. When I dreamed about catching the biggest fish in the river, I ended up ruining my dad's fishing trip.

In my dream on Thursday night, I was the star of *The Terrific Tale of Tara, the*

Proud Fairy Princess. Miles kept shouting, "Trees rule the world!" and people were clapping and cheering for me. Betty and Booker were jumping up and down. The sixth graders were giving each other high fives. Even Crawford Mills and Lilac Starr

were applauding. I woke up with a smile on my face.

The day started out great. Doofus Doolittle licked my nose as soon as I opened my eyes. I wore my star earrings, green-and-orange skirt, and lucky red socks. Tina was already at breakfast when I came downstairs. My dad was going to drive her to school early because she needed to help Mrs. White get ready for the dress rehearsal.

"Tina, you're the greatest!" I yelled out as she went through the door. It was best not to say the words *good luck*. They might remind her of her good-luck charm.

Tina turned around and grinned. "You're the greatest too, Willie. See you at school." It was just like old times.

My dad had made his special pancakes for breakfast because it was a special day. My mom sat across from me as I finished eating. "Your dad and I are so proud of you and Tina," she said as she drank her coffee. "When we pick you up after the show tonight, we're going to go out to dinner. How does pizza sound?"

"Great!" I said. "Can we get ice cream afterward?"

"Anything you two want," my mom said.

I smiled all the way to the bus. I could almost taste the tomato sauce.

But I had the rest of the day to get through.

The big dress rehearsal was starting at two. Everyone in the whole school was going to be there. All the kids in the play were nervous, even me, although all I had to do was stand and sway. At 1 P.M. Mrs. White's voice came over the PA system.

"All children playing trees, please report to the auditorium for your costumes at once," she said.

Lilac Starr and Crawford Mills had received their costumes several days before. They had been in the auditorium rehearsing since morning.

Lilac's words about my costume concerned me. I was worried as I walked into the auditorium.

All the trees wore brown pants or tights, which were supposed to look like tree trunks. The saplings wore big floppy hats covered with paper leaves. The oaks had green top hats and paper leaves attached to their sleeves. The weeping willows had the best costumes of all. We wore big sheets that reached below our knees. Coming out of our heads were long, thin, strips of paper that were cut to look like the long, dripping branches of willow trees. When we swayed back and forth, the paper made a swishing sound, just like willow leaves blowing in the wind.

"This is great!" said one of the weeping willows as he swayed back and forth.

"Sure is!" I said. I waved my arms up and down. I loved the way the leaves sounded.

"All actors take deep breaths and get

ready. Princess Tara, Prince Igor, Elves, Giant. That means you!" Mrs. White yelled.

Everyone could hear the audience filing into the auditorium. It was weird being behind the curtain and listening to kids laughing and talking as they came in. One of the elves began to cry.

"Stage fright!" whispered Gregory Greene—Max the wise giant.

"He'd better get over it!" said Lilac Starr.

"Trees, take your places, now!" Mrs. White yelled.

I caught a glimpse of Tina talking to Crawford Mills. Crawford kept putting his hand around his throat. Then I saw Tina talking to Bill Taylor and, finally, to Mrs. White. When Tina saw me, she waved. This was my sister's big day and I was really happy for her.

"Get ready, weeping willows!" Mrs. White said. She had told us not to cover our faces until we stood on our Xs. We all put our hoods over our heads, followed by the paper leaves.

We all held our breath. We all were very quiet. The CD began to play over the loud-speaker. There was a hush in the audience. Slowly the curtain began to rise.

First Gregory Greene, Max the wise giant, walked across the stage. The cute little elves scampered around him. I knew that Booker and Betty were nervous, but they were doing the best that they could. I wished that there was a way I could tell them. Crawford, Prince Igor, came onstage next. His lines were the first words spoken in the play. Crawford's voice sounded scratchy, as if he might have a sore throat, but nobody seemed to notice.

Then Lilac, Tara the proud fairy princess, came onstage. The audience gasped in amazement!

"Wow! What a beautiful dress!" I heard somebody say.

"I wish I could be her," another kid said.

Lilac held her head very high. She stepped in tiny, dainty steps as she took her place. But when she saw me on my X, she narrowed her eyes and poked out her mouth. I knew then there was going to be trouble.

STEP #8:
Quit Dreaming— You're a Tree!

"Move back!" Lilac said out of the side of her mouth. She spoke in a whisper. A *loud* whisper.

"I'm standing on my X," I whispered back.

She turned to face the audience. "I am Tara, the proud fairy princess!"

Gregory—Max the wise giant—bowed.

The audience applauded.

"You are proud, but are you wise?" Max asked Tara.

"And who are you?" Tara asked Igor, the mean, evil prince.

"I am Igor. I will soon be king of all the land!"

Then it was the cute little elves' turn. They skipped around the stage. Then they began to dance. Lilac looked back at me.

"Move it!" she said out of the corner of her mouth.

"Mrs. White told me to stay where I was, and that's what I'm doing," I said in a low voice.

Lilac turned her attention back to the play.

"I am Igor, the great prince. I have strength. You have none!" Crawford said. His voice sounded as if it hurt him to talk.

"But I command the woods and forests!"

84

Princess Tara said to Prince Igor.

That was the cue for me and the other weeping willows to sway. When I moved to the left, Lilac stepped on my right toe. Hard.

"Ouch!" I said.

"Your leaves hit me in the face!" Lilac said under her breath.

"I'm on my X, and don't you dare step on my toe again!" I said.

One of the saplings giggled. I hoped the audience hadn't heard us, too.

"We are all visitors in this beautiful forest," said Max, the wise giant. "It doesn't belong to any of us. Nobody can own the trees."

That was the cue for the weeping willows to shake our arms so our leaves would flutter.

But when I shook my arm, my leaves
hit Lilac in the face.

"Achoo!" she sneezed. "Achoo! Achoo!
Achoo! Your leaves are making me sneeze!"
she said.

"Sorry!" I whispered, stepping away from

her so my leaves wouldn't get in her face.

That was a big mistake!

"Hey, did you see that! That tree is walking!" somebody shouted from the audience.

"Hey, the tree walked. The tree walked!"

"Yeah, trees rule the earth!" one of the sixth graders yelled. Some kids in the front row heard him, and they started chanting, "Trees rule the earth! Trees rule the earth!"

"Get back!" Lilac whispered to me. I stepped back as far as I could.

"Hey, that tree walked again!" somebody said.

"Go, tree! Go, tree! Go, tree!" a bunch of kids started yelling.

"Trees rule the earth!" somebody yelled out again.

Lilac sneezed so hard her crown fell off her head.

Suddenly everybody in the audience was laughing. A couple of sixth graders started to whistle.

I stood perfectly still and held my breath. What was going to happen next?

Mrs. Morris, the principal, jumped out of her seat and rushed to the front of the room. She stood in front of the stage and clapped her hands six times. Then she put her hands on her hips and stared hard at every kid who was laughing.

"There will be order in this room! There will be order in this room!" she said.

Everybody stopped laughing. Everybody was quiet. Nobody wanted to cross Mrs. Morris. Even the sixth graders behaved.

"This play will continue!" she said. Then she sat back down.

The next line belonged to Prince Igor. But when Crawford opened his mouth to speak, his voice was so scratchy you couldn't hear what he was saying.

"Crawford, speak louder!" Mrs. White whispered from the wings. His voice came out in a croak.

Then the giggles started. When one person starts, the giggles jump from one person to the next. And that's what happened. The elves began to giggle. Then the giggles hopped to the saplings, and nothing could make them stop. Then the oaks. And the willows.

Finally, the play was over. The audience applauded. I guess they'd had a good time. But we were just glad to see the curtain come down. The moment it hit the floor, Tina came running on stage.

"My play is ruined!" she screamed. Then she glared at me.

"Willie, if you had moved back when Lilac told you to, then Lilac wouldn't have started sneezing, and the elves wouldn't have started giggling, and—" She put her hands over her face.

I looked down at the floor. Tina was right. Why hadn't I just done what Lilac said?

After the audience had left the auditorium, Mrs. White called us all together. She told us to sit in a circle.

"What happened today was nobody's fault," she said. "Yesterday, I really didn't take the time to explain to Willie where she should stand. She stood where her X was, which was the right thing to do. And Lilac didn't mean to sneeze. She couldn't help it."

"The elves and saplings shouldn't have giggled!" said Gregory Greene.

"I think the audience thought that was part of the play," Mrs. White said. "Sometimes things happen in a play that you can't control. But as long as it works, it's okay." Everyone laughed at that. Maybe things hadn't been as bad as they seemed.

"This afternoon was only a dress rehearsal. We have a saying in theater that a bad dress rehearsal always means a great opening night. I'm sure that's what will happen tonight."

Everybody was feeling a little bit better. Maybe Mrs. White was right. Even Tina looked relieved.

"So we're going to run through the play, from beginning to end, one last time, and then we'll all be ready for opening night. But first take the hand of the person sitting next to you," Mrs. White said.

Gregory was sitting on one side of me

and Booker was on the other. It felt strange holding hands with Booker and Gregory, but it made me feel strong, too.

"Now, we're going to go around the circle, and every one of you is going to say these words: We are a team!"

"We are a team!" said Tina.

"We are a team!" said Betty.

"We are a team!" said Lilac.

Then it was Crawford Mills's turn to speak. When he opened his mouth, no words came out.

STEP #9:
Forget Step #8. Fairy Tales Always Have Happy Endings!

We all stared at Crawford.

"Are you all right?" Mrs. White asked.

"I can't talk!" Crawford squeaked.

Mrs. White told one of the sixth graders to run to the nurse's office to get Mrs. Lois, our school nurse. When she came into the auditorium, she rushed to Crawford and placed her hand on his forehead.

"Oh, my goodness!" she said, snatching

her hand off Crawford's head. "You have a high fever. You're burning up!"

Crawford moved his lips. Mrs. Lois bent down to hear what he said. She looked up at Mrs. White.

"This boy is sick!" she said. "He's hot and he has a sore throat. I'm going to call his mother to come and get him right away!'

"No-o-o-o!" said Crawford.

"Yes!" said Mrs. Lois.

Mrs. Lois looked at Mrs. White. They both looked at Crawford. Mrs. White shook her head. "This is bad news," she said in a low voice.

Crawford and Mrs. Lois left for her office so that she could call his mother. The rest of us just stood there.

Lilac threw up her hands. "Just my luck!" she said.

"*Your* luck? What about poor Crawford? He's the one who has a fever. He's the one who is sick!" said Gregory.

"What are we going to do now?" asked Booker.

"Bill, I think it might be up to you," said Mrs. White.

We all looked at Bill Taylor. He was the person who was supposed to play Prince Igor if Crawford was sick. Now the play depended on him.

Bill looked scared. He looked worried. He stared down at his feet.

"Bill?" Mrs. White said in a quiet voice.

"I don't know the lines," Bill said. "I wasn't paying attention. I didn't think Crawford was going to be sick. I don't know what to do."

"Are you willing to try to do the part?" Mrs. White asked.

Bill nodded that he was. But he still looked worried.

Mrs. White gave a long sigh. I glanced at Tina. She looked like she was about to cry.

"Everybody ready? Let's start our rehearsal now," said Mrs. White.

We all got into our places. Bill said the first few lines of the play. But then he had to read the script. He sounded like he was reading a story instead of speaking the lines. He didn't *act* like Prince Igor. Everyone tried very hard to do their parts right. Everybody did what they were supposed to do. Except for Bill Taylor. I felt sorry for him. Prince Igor was a really important character. The play didn't work without him.

When we finished, nobody said anything.

I looked around for Tina. She was sitting in the last row in the auditorium. Even though I couldn't see her face, I knew how sad she must feel.

"Bill, I think you will have to read from the script tonight," Mrs. White said. Then she turned toward the rest of us. "Before the play opens, I'll go out and explain to the audience that one of our lead characters suddenly took ill, and his understudy will read his part. Come on, everybody, let's get out of our costumes, and I'll see everybody back here in time for our performance tonight." She tried to sound cheerful, but her face didn't look that way.

"What do you mean Bill is going to read from the script?" Lilac asked.

"Just what I said, Lilac," said Mrs. White.

"That's going to sound dumb!" one of the first graders said.

"Everybody is going to laugh at us!" said Betty.

"This is going to be *so* embarrassing," said Lilac.

I felt sorry for Bill, but I couldn't think of anything to say that would make him feel better.

"Let's not do it. Let's postpone it until Crawford comes back!" said one of the fifth graders.

"It's too late to postpone it," said Mrs. White. "The notices have all gone out. Everybody is coming tonight. It's perfectly fine for an understudy to take over for one of the stars. It happens all the time in the theater."

"Yeah, but the understudy always

knows his lines!" Gregory said.

"It's going to throw off the whole play!" said Lilac. Bill looked like he was going to cry.

"That's enough, everybody!" Mrs. White said.

"Tina, what do you think we should do?" Gregory asked.

Slowly, Tina walked to the front of the room and climbed up on the stage. I have never felt as sorry for her as I did then.

"Everything is wrong," she said in a small voice. "Bill doesn't know his lines. It's not his fault; he didn't know that Crawford was going to get sick all of a sudden. Everybody laughed during the dress rehearsal because Willie moved and Lilac sneezed. Maybe we should just forget the whole thing!"

I came over to Tina and put my arm around her.

"Don't feel bad, Tina. This is a really good play," I said.

"But nobody will know it!" she said. "This will be the last play I'll ever write!"

"You can't just give up!"

"Who says?"

"I say!"

"Why not?"

"Because I can play the part of Prince Igor!" There was somebody else who knew Igor's lines. And that somebody was me!

"But you're a girl!" said Lilac.

"Who cares!" said Gregory.

"I know all the lines that Crawford has to say," I said. "I know what he has to do.

I'll tie up my braids and tuck them under my crown!"

"I don't want to be the princess if Willie Thomas is going to be the prince," sniffed Lilac.

"That's great, because I know *your* lines too!" said Ruby, Lilac's understudy.

"Okay! I guess I'll be the princess," said Lilac.

"Don't do us any favors. Even princesses can be replaced," said Gregory. He picked up Prince Igor's crown and placed it on my head. "I crown you Prince Igor!"

Everybody applauded, and Tina smiled a bright, wide, happy smile. Mrs. White gave me a pat on the back. "Come on, kids, let's give it another try!" she said.

Crawford's costume was too big, so Mrs. White took it home to wash it and take it in for me. Lilac was taller than me, but who said a prince has to be taller than a princess? The rehearsal that afternoon was great, and opening night was even better. It was fun saying Igor's lines. I hadn't noticed it before, but he had the best lines in the play. They got the most laughs.

The audience gave us four curtain calls, and Mrs. Morris presented Tina with a big bouquet of pink and red roses. I was really proud to be Igor, even though I wasn't listed in the program. The best, though, was yet to come.

When I took my bow, I spotted something in a shiny plastic case near the lights in the front of the stage. You guessed it! It was Tina's good-luck charm, waiting to be discovered. As soon as the curtain dropped, I picked it up and gave it to Tina.

"You lost it, didn't you?" She peered at me as if she were reading my mind.

"Yeah. I didn't want to tell you because I was afraid you'd be mad at me."

"I *am* mad that you lost my lucky charm," Tina said, then grinned. "But you saved my play and you're the only sister I've got, so I have to forgive you." She divided her bouquet of flowers and gave half to me.

"For a good frog, a better prince, and the very best sister in the whole, wide world!" Tina said with a bow. Then she grabbed my hand and off we ran to find our mom and dad.

Tina and I ate three slices of pizza each! That's the most we've ever eaten at one time. There were only two slices to bring home. Tina was glad to have her lucky charm back. I was glad she had it too, since it only brought me BAD luck. The next week, the school newspaper interviewed Tina about the play. I copied down my favorite part: "Willimena Thomas, my sister and a third grader in Mrs. Sweetly's class, saved the school play when she stood in for Crawford Mills, the evil prince, who was sent home sick." Can you believe Tina said that? I guess fairy tales really do have happy endings and frogs still turn into princes! So, back off, Lilac Starr—there's a new star at Harriet Tubman, and her name is WILLIMENA!

Willie

P.S.: So sunny skies are here again! But my scariest holiday is on the horizon—and it's not Halloween. Would you believe . . . Valentine's Day!?!

Why does Valentine's Da
give Willie the creeps?
Read all about it in . . .
WILLIMENA RULES!
23 Ways to Mess U
Valentine's Day
Rule Book #5